AZTEC QUEST

by
Herbie Brennan

Kingfisher

Kingfisher
An imprint of Larousse plc
Elsley House
24-30 Great Titchfield Street
London
W1P 7AD

10 9 8 7 6 5 4 3 2 1

A CIP catalogue record for this book is available from the British
Library.

ISBN 0 7534 0087 1

Designed and typeset by Val Carless
Printed in the United Kingdom

It's the year of 1-Reed, 1519. The mighty Aztec Empire is reeling under the onslaught of invaders from the East. Thousands have been slaughtered. Thousands more maimed and wounded. Whole populations are fleeing the carnage. People are predicting the end of the world.

But you have troubles of your own. Your family, poor Tlaxcalan farmers, have joined the invaders in the hope of overthrowing the Aztec tyranny. And you have managed to get yourself captured in your very first battle.

Now you're languishing in a filthy dungeon waiting for the priests to come. Because the Aztec First Speaker and Emperor, Montezuma II, has decreed that only a human sacrifice can halt the brutal invaders ... and you're it!

Already the High Priest is trying to decide whether to roast you alive or let you off lightly by cutting open your chest with an obsidian knife and ripping out your still-beating heart.

Can you escape to rejoin your family? Can you elude the priests as you flee through the ruins of this terrifying city?

Find out, as you adventure through one of the most frightening periods of human history in this incredible new game book.

IMPORTANT: READ THIS FIRST!

You can't just read this book – you have to live it.

To do that, you'll need to keep a record of any weapons, magic potions, and so on, that you find, along with your number of Life Points. You'll also need a couple of dice.

Of course, you may have played another of the books in this series. In which case you'll know exactly how to play. But if this is your first book, turn to the back of the book to the section headed GAME PLAY SYSTEM.

Otherwise, you can turn to the next page and get straight on with your adventure ...

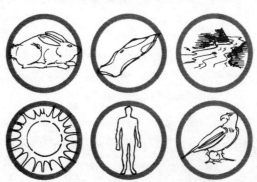

Darkness. You've opened your eyes to total darkness. Your head hurts as if somebody recently bashed it with a club. Which, now you come to think of it, was exactly what happened.

As you explore the confines of your tiny cell, your memory gradually returns. You remember how you joined the iron-clad invaders from the East, hoping to help them overthrow the evil Emperor Montezuma, whose very name means Angry Lord. You remember how you were stunned and captured, and brought here to Tenochtitlán, the Aztec capital.

Most of all you remember how the Angry Lord has ordered a human sacrifice to persuade the gods to turn away the invaders.

And you are going to be it!

The guard arrives. "I got some food for you," he growls.

This could be your chance to escape. You know Tenochtitlán like the back of your hand, so if you can only get out of this cell, you can quickly lose yourself in its winding alleys and hordes of people. To launch an attack on your guard, go to 18. But maybe it would make more sense to eat the food since you're feeling so weak, in which case go to 26.

Splat! The stone's fallen down and crushed you.
Toss yourself like a pancake to section 13.

Enough of fumbling! Bravely you stride forward. Bravely you tumble downwards to splat onto hard rock far below. You lie there wondering if you are dead.

Good point. Throw two dice. Score 2 and you're definitely dead at 13. Score anything else and deduct your score from your Life Points. If this kills you, go to 13. If it doesn't, rub your bruises at 105.

You step over the limp body of the jaguar. The fight was noisy and the great cat howled when you eventually killed him, so you're worried the priests may have heard.

It may make sense to get out of here at once. If you think so, turn to the map at 33 and pick another destination. Alternatively, you might try hiding in the pyramid to the west at 49. But there's a third possibility. During the fight you noticed a tiny overgrown doorway in the southern wall of the fortress. It probably leads back outside, but you can find out for sure at 82.

Phew! It looked like a little pyramid, but it's actually a long way up. You're standing on a platform at the summit of the smaller pyramid, only to discover this is just a stopping off point.

A flight of stone steps that seems to go on forever will take you to the upper terraces of the larger pyramid, while a gloomy entrance looks as if it actually leads inside the pyramid.

Meanwhile you'd better decide what you want to do about that little skunk that's backing towards you with its tail up.

The skunk only has 10 Life Points, but that's not really the point is it? If you start a fight now and it gets in a first strike, you're going to pong for the next fifty sections. You can try making friends with the skunk at 32. Or running blindly from it at 59. Or, if you insist on thinking with your glands, you can start a fight at 98.

6

The ants are delicious, but the chilli on the maguey grubs is a little hot for your taste. Are you really going to eat the rats in chocolate sauce?

If you are, go to 41. If not, try 55.

7

Half blinded, smelling to high heaven, choking, coughing and with an incredibly bad taste in your mouth, you stagger out of this ghastly little building into the brilliant sunlight.

Just in time to be attacked by a jaguar attracted by the smell.

Is this mess never going to end? The jag has 50 Life Points and fights at +5 claw and +10 fang damage. If the beast kills you, he will drag your body to 13. If not, you are at long last safe to return to 33 and select another destination.

8

"So what's the deal here?" you call in the direction of the mysterious voice. "I mean, how often do I have to play? Do I get one of the new horses the Spanish are bringing in?"

The voice calls back, "You mightn't have to play any more than just one game. Money for old aloe rope! And if you hitch up to a winning team, you get all the perks. Copal, amber, jewels, silver, gold, featherwork, crystal ... anything you could want!"

So how does that sound to you? If you figure you've a future in the ball game, you can go off with the talent scout at 159. If not, you can politely decline at 83.

9

Cautiously, silently, you creep towards the sleeping snake. Slowly, so very slowly, you reach out one trembling hand to tug away the ornamental armour.

The snake opens one eye and grins at you evilly.

Looks as if you're in for a punch-up here. The rattler has only 25 Life Points, but makes up for that with an extra violent poison which not only removes Life Points at +10 on a successful strike, but continues to remove 5 Life Points on each of your turns thereafter until the fight is over, whether or not the snake ever strikes you again.

If this unfortunate encounter kills you, go to 13. If you survive, collect your reward not in heaven but at 22.

Good grief, this is a spot of luck! You've found the road home! There's no doubt about it, this road leads you out of Teotihuacán westwards, and unless you're very much mistaken, it will carry you safely through the jungle all the way back to your home territory and blessed freedom! No more fleeing from the priests! No more worries about becoming a human sacrifice!

Gaily you begin to skip down the road. Gaily you trot round a corner. Gaily you walk straight into a roadblock manned by several hundred heavily armed Aztec warriors in ornamental silver armour under surcoats of featherwork, an élite guard if ever you saw one.

Their leader saunters over to you. "Let's see your special pass, young one," he demands.

Don't even think about taking on these characters. You'd be dead of exhaustion by the time you'd made all the dice rolls. If you happen to have a special pass, flash it at the guard and make off to 102. If not, your only option is to slouch to 33 and pick another destination.

"Hup, one, two, three! Hup, one, two, three! Pick it up there! Look lively, lads!"

These hearty instructions are being issued by Prince Nezahualcoyotl, the character with the smooth line of chat and the fancy armour. His name, one of the soldiers mentions, means 'Hungry Fox' which you decide just about sums him up.

"Excuse me, Prince," you ask while trying to keep up, "but where are we going?"

"Tenochtitlán," Prince Nezahualcoyotl tells you tersely. Then, because he's actually incapable of being terse about anything, he adds, "The Big Apple, Sacrifice Central, seven and a half square kilometres of sheer heaven built a mere one hundred and seventy-four years ago on a marshy island on the Lake of the Moon."

So you're being taken to the Aztec capital. This is not good news. The place is crawling with priests and sacrificial altars.

"Prince Nez –" you begin.

But the man is in full flight and will not be stopped. "Guided by our god Huitzilopochtli, who frequently takes the form of a hummingbird (which you should appreciate, young person, since your parents have blessed you with that name) our people surmounted insurmountable odds to replicate the ancient capital of mystic Aztlan, from where we originated and there –

"PRINCE NEZAHUALCOYOTL!" you scream in desperation.

He looks at you in surprise. "Yes?"

"Can you tell me something about the ball game I'll be in?"

"Can I tell you something about the ball game? What I don't know about the ball game, you wouldn't want to know."

"He's right," puts in one of the soldiers. "Knows all there is to know about the ball game."

This is like pulling teeth, but you persevere. "Then tell me, Prince."

Prince Nezahualcoyotl smiles broadly at you. "It's called Ollin, the Sacred Cosmic Ball Game. Most popular sport in the whole Aztec Empire. Big crowds, royal patrons, lots of fun. Except for the losing team, of course."

"Why," you ask innocently, "what happens to the losing team?"

"We kill them," Prince Nezahualcoyotl grins.

You're going to have to get out of this. Unless you think it's worth the risk of death to enjoy all that fame and money as a big star of Ollin the Sacred Cosmic Ball Game. There's no chance you can fight your way out from under this heavy-duty escort, but it's a long march to the capital, so you may be able to escape tonight while they're asleep at 25. But if you're feeling lucky and want to take your chances at the game, you can march into Tenochtitlán with Prince Nezahualcoyotl and his men at 54.

This is sort of interesting. The way to get up seems to be to climb a flight of steps on one side to the first terrace, then walk all the way round the back to the next steps which take you to the second terrace. And so on, so you keep circling round the pyramid as you climb it – just like the pyramids the Aztecs have built in Tenochtitlán, their capital.

You begin the hazardous climb upwards ...

And hazardous it is, since these steps are old and crumbling. Try an Absolutely Anything Roll to see if you make it safely to the top. If you succeed, go to 155. If you fail, I'm afraid it's back to 33 to pick another destination (or this one again if you're feeling stubborn). If you die in the attempt, scream horribly all the way to 13.

You're dead!

Fortunately you don't have to stay that way. Roll up another batch of Life Points and go back to Section 1 and start again. Better luck next time!

How irritating. This isn't a passageway at all. In fact it's little more than an elongated antechamber. There are a few chips of flint on the floor, but otherwise it's empty.

Unless you want to search for a secret passage at 111, your only option is to go back to 105 and try another exit.

Making Your Aztec Deathmatch Board Game

First, draw a grid of 9 x 11 squares on a large piece of paper or cardboard. You may, if you wish, give your grid a border decorated with Aztec numbers as shown on page 12. Mark the Cosmic Square with a coloured pen.

Now turn to page 4 where you'll find drawings of the pieces. Trace these onto light card and colour them in as follows; skull, vulture, crocodile, monkey, jaguar, reed, rainstorm, windstorm, flint and rabbit should have dark backgrounds. Water, eagle, lizard, sun, deer, dog, flower, house, Quetzalcóatl and grass should have light backgrounds. Cut all the pieces out and set them on the board as shown on the next page.

AZTEC DEATHMATCH BOARD GAME

The Players

There are two players in the game – Quetzalcóatl (you) who moves the light pieces, representing Life, and Tezcatlipoca (your opponent) who moves the dark pieces, representing Death. Strictly speaking, MAN is on the side of neither Life nor Death, but throughout the game, the MAN piece is moved exclusively by Life.

Object of the Game

Unusually in a board game, the two players have totally different objectives. For Quetzalcóatl, the objective of the game is to place MAN on the Cosmic Square. For Tezcatlipoca, the objective is to remove MAN from the board.

Rules of Play

1. The two players roll dice to start the game. Highest score makes the first move.
2. Players move in turns until the game is concluded.
3. No piece may pass through a square occupied by another piece.
4. The MAN piece may not be moved onto a threatened square.
5. When you take an opponent's piece, your (taking) piece ends up on the square previously occupied by your opponent. Your opponent's piece is removed from the board.
6. The game is won for Quetzalcóatl when the MAN piece arrives on the Cosmic Square. It is won for Tezcatlipoca when the MAN piece is removed from the board.

Movement of the pieces

Grass and Skull – any number of squares horizontally or vertically in any direction.

Vulture, Crocodile, House and Quetzalcóatl – any number of squares diagonally in any direction.

Monkey, Jaguar, Reed, Deer, Dog and Flower – one square in any direction horizontally, vertically or diagonally.

Rainstorm, Windstorm, Flint, Rabbit, Water, Eagle, Lizard, Sun – one square forward until they can go no further. When blocked, these pieces may be about-faced to move in the opposite direction, but about-facing counts as a move in itself. Note: these pieces take diagonally, like pawns in chess.

MAN - one square in any direction, including diagonally. It is illegal to move this piece onto a threatened square.

Remember, in this game you must always play Quetzalcóatl. If you lose the game, go to 13. If you win, celebrate wildly at 38.

Boy, was this a mistake! As you approach the gigantic Pyramid of the Sun, you realise you've walked straight into no fewer than six Aztec priests!

"It's Hummingbird!" shouts one of them. "It's the one the Angry Lord has ordered us to sacrifice!"

At which all six of them hurl themselves upon you.

Your name is really Hummingbird? But no time to worry about that now. The reason Aztec priests run around in sixes is that they need five to hold you down – one on each arm and leg and one on your head – while the sixth cuts your heart out.

One of the priests has 60 Life Points, two have 50 each and the remaining three have 40 each. The toughest of them is armed with a +10 sword and the others have +5 clubs. The only good news is they're not trying to kill you, so if your Life Points drop below 10, consider yourself knocked unconscious and go to 71. If they kill you accidentally go to 13. If a miracle happens and you manage to beat these guys, go to 90.

You walk out into the blinding sunlight with your fellow players, and at once a roar of appreciation and applause swells from the audience around the stadium. Your colleagues are a motley crew – unwilling slaves, prisoners of war, condemned criminals and a few other dregs. The opposing team, by contrast, all look like seasoned athletes, a fact that doesn't exactly give you a whole heap of confidence.

The stadium looks even bigger now than it did yesterday when Prince Nezahualcoyotl marched you round it for your first view, before locking you in a cell beneath the public stands. It's stone built, and high-walled to prevent players escaping when their luck starts to run against them.

Yesterday the court was unmarked, but in the night game officials have set up twenty stone hoops in two diagonal lines of ten, and placed huge wooden idols to mark the cardinal points of east, south, west and north at the four corners of the court.

An official hands you your mask and you pull it on. Every player in the court is obliged to wear a special mask to represent a particular character in the game. Yours is the mask of cuetzpallin the lizard, representing fertility. Others are issued with masks like ozomatl, the monkey or enecatl, the windstorm, representing violence. There are enthusiastic cheers and catcalls from the crowd as the players don their gear.

"Tezcatlipoca team take your places!" roars an official with a voice that carries half-way to the Gulf of Mexico.

You watch with trepidation as the opposing team moves into place. Apart from the masks and loincloths they are wearing nothing, so you can see every bulging muscle of their bodies. These guys look far tougher, far faster, far more powerful than the rag-tag and bobtail of your own team. Not for the first time you wonder about your chances of winning.

"Quetzalcóatl team take your places!" roars the same official just as loudly.

You move to take your place beside one of the hoops. With everyone in place, the two teams form a giant X across the court. Several players start jogging on the spot to warm up. You lick your lips, which have suddenly gone dry.

There is an instant hush across the entire stadium as a tall priest walks onto the court. Instinctively you look around for a place to hide, then remember you're wearing a mask now so no priest will recognise you. This one is carrying a mask of his own, a flat, partially bearded face of Man, the representative of all humanity. He holds it up and the crowd cheers. He puts it on and the crowd cheers again. Then he walks to his place at the centre of the two diagonals. An official sprints across and hands him a heavy solid rubber ball.

"Let the Sacred Cosmic Ball Game of Ollin the Sun begin!" shouts the masked priest and tosses the heavy ball into play.

The rules of the game are simple. You score by getting the ball through an opponent's hoop. If you drop the ball, you die. If you fail to get it through a hoop, you die. If your team loses, you die.

With a heavy sigh you trot forward to get your hands on the ball.

You realise there's a fair chance you're not going to survive this game? Make a modified Absolutely Anything Roll, but this one time read your score as follows:

● Score 2 , 3, 4 or 5 and you failed to survive even the first half of the game. Go directly to 13.
● Score 6, 7, 8 or 9 and you make it through to half time, but must make a second roll to determine if you survive the second half. In this second roll, a score of 2, 3, 4, 5, or 6 means death (go to 13) while 7, 8, 9, 10, 11, or 12 indicates you survive the whole game and can go to 38.
● Score 10, 11 or 12 and you survive to stagger off to 38.

With fists flying, you throw yourself on your guard.

Your guard is tough. He has 40 Life Points and carries a sword that gives 6 extra points of damage on every successful hit. If you attack before eating, you're so weak you must subtract 3 from every damage score you make. If the guard kills you, go to 13. If you win your fight, turn to 33.

You look around you as you leave the stadium. There's only one way you really want to go – out of this city! You've survived so far against all the odds, but that doesn't guarantee you're going to stay lucky. What you definitely need to do now is head for the hills, get back to your own people and, hopefully, rejoin the rebellion against the dreaded Aztec Empire.

But where to go? Study the map of Tenochtitlán on the facing page and decide which destination will suit you best.

TENOCHTITLÁN

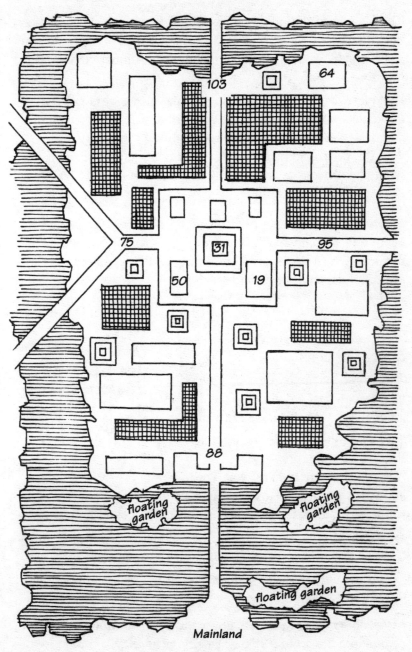

103

64

75

31

95

50

19

88

floating garden

floating garden

floating garden

Mainland

20

There's a horrid grinding noise and the stone slab slowly moves upwards, revealing an ominously dark entrance. Cautiously you move inside, wondering at the ingenious machinery that raised the stone.

As your eyes become accustomed to the gloom, you can see broken slabs and pillars, the remains of a once-great temple. But clearly it is a temple that has not been used for generations. You could poke around here for hours, but with the slab now open it would be obvious to any passing priest that somebody has solved the secret of the pyramid.

All the same, you can risk staying a little longer to search the temple by turning to 61. But if you want to play it safe, get out while the going's good by turning to 33 to select a different destination from the map.

21

"Settle down, youngster! You're in no danger any more!"

The words reach you through a blood-red mist as you cast around desperately to escape. But your efforts are in vain.

"Aren't you the hero of the Cosmic Ball Game?" the priest asks you. "We never meant to harm you, you know. It's just that we had instructions to bring you to the Emperor for a chat and afternoon chocolate. I can't imagine why you fought us so vigorously."

"Sorry," you mutter, scarcely able to believe your luck.

"Think nothing of it," says the priest. "But now you must come to meet our Emperor!"

At which he leads you back down the pyramid and across the central square to the Emperor's Palace at 50.

22

This armour looks good, that's for sure. But gold, which is a soft metal, isn't the best material for the job, so it only deducts 3 points of any damage scored against you while you're wearing it. No wonder the Spaniards are making mincemeat of the Aztecs – their armour is made from iron, which is a whole lot better than anything the Aztecs have.

All the same, any protection is better than none. Take your booty and trog off to 33 where you can select another destination.

23

You cut your way through some intrusive undergrowth and find yourself in the courtyard of an immense fortress, so large that it actually houses its own great stepped pyramid to the west. The massive stone walls of the fortress tower around you. Here at least you will be safe from the priests, for it is obvious from the thick vegetation growing everywhere that no human has ventured within these walls for years.

No human, but there is a rather nasty jaguar stalking you from the direction of the pyramid. No use running – this thing would be faster than you are, even if you stole a Spanish horse. The brute has 50 Life Points and attacks at +5 on account of vicious teeth and claws. If you survive the attack, turn to 4. If not, go with great reluctance to 13.

24

The guard leads you through an entranceway and into an astonishing pleasure garden. Despite your worries, your soul responds at once to the panorama of trees, flowering shrubs and beds of flowers.

"This way," mutters the guard, seemingly immune to the beauty of the place. He leads you along a maze of stone walks that intersect the garden.

Suddenly a ghastly scream sounds close to hand. You stop abruptly, but the guard only shakes his head in amusement. "Don't worry," he says. "We're passing Lord Montezuma's menagerie. That's just one of the beasts he keeps as pets."

"Are there many?" you ask curiously.

"Birds, serpents, jaguars – you wouldn't believe how many animals he keeps. More than three hundred slaves are assigned just to look after them. And that's not to mention the fish."

"Fish?" you echo.

The guard nods to one side. Your eyes follow the direction he indicates, and you discover, set into the expanse of the garden, a broad, stone-lined pond.

Moments later you are in the main building of the palace itself. The corridors and chambers you pass through are imposing, but your mind remains filled with the sights, smells and sounds of the pleasure garden.

The guard stops.

"We're here. The Angry Lord is waiting for you through that door. I just thought you might like a moment to collect yourself before meeting him."

Well, would you? If so, you can meditate a while at 53. But if you'd prefer to get the confrontation over with straight away, stride forward bravely into 78.

Patiently you wait as the sun sinks beyond the western horizon. Patiently you wait as the men bed down. Patiently you wait until Prince Nezahualcoyotl stops talking and begins to doze. Then, with a silent prayer, you creep away into the night.

But will you get away with it? Make an Absolutely Anything Roll. If you die in the attempt, go to 13. If you fail and can't try again, you're stuck with marching into Tenochtitlán with the Prince and his men at 54. If you succeed, keep creeping patiently to 60.

Strange smells waft up from the bowls on the tray as the guard sets it carefully on the baked earth floor. "Maguey grubs with chilli, winged ants with savoury herbs, and rats in chocolate sauce to follow," he announces cheerfully. "Nothing but the best when you're going to be sacrificed."

You stare woodenly at these Aztec delicacies.

If you simply can't face this menu, you can always try to strangle the guard at 18. If you can't wait to taste rats in chocolate sauce, turn to 6.

 27

"Sir!" you cry. "It was I! I was that young sacrifice who escaped! It was I who ran rings round your priests and defeated your warriors. It was I who fought and stole and looted and despised everything you stand for. But I cannot bear to have sixty-nine thousand, nine hundred and ninety-nine lives on my conscience, so I hearby admit to my identity.

I do this in the near certain knowledge that you, Great Lord, will be so impressed by my valour that you will not only rescind the sacrifice order, but quite possibly make me your chief advisor or even general of your armed forces – as frequently happens in adventures of this type."

"If you believe that, you must believe in Santa Claus," Montezuma remarks.

At which he orders you an immediate heart transplant into a convenient bucket. Go to 13.

The torchlight flickers on the walls and it's obvious this is no natural passageway. Somebody hacked this place out of solid bedrock. Unfortunately they didn't hack it very far, because after you've gone a short distance you reach a dead end.

This hasn't been entirely futile, however, since you discover a sealed container of chocolate drink in one corner.

Which not only tastes good, but does you good. One drink will restore a single die roll of Life Points, and there are three drinks in the container. Not bad at all, but unless you want to search for a secret passage at 111, your only option now is to go back to 105 and try another exit.

Splat! The stone's fallen down and crushed you.

Toss yourself like a pancake to section 13.

"I think actually, sir, I'd better be going," you say diplomatically. "I mean I know how busy you are organising sacrifices and suchlike, and I wouldn't want to outstay my welcome." It strikes you that Montezuma is a fruit and nut case who'd have been locked up in the funny farm years ago if he hadn't been made Emperor at an early stage of his career. Certainly his behaviour is far from sane and you feel that the sooner you're out of his presence the better.

"Oh, yes, well, off you go then," Montezuma mutters, losing interest at once. He waves his hand in dismissal.

You bow deeply and back out of the throne room. You close the door behind you, hardly able to believe your luck. You've escaped with a whole skin. This is too good to be true!

You look around you and realise it really *is* too good to be true. The guard who brought you to the throne room is nowhere in sight. There are two passageways and a closed door leading off from where you're standing. Which to take? There's no question of returning to the throne room and asking for directions. You're going to have to make up your own mind and risk getting lost in Montezuma's Palace.

corridor runs north to 72, the other runs east to 84 while the door opens onto 104.

Are you out of your mind? This is the Great Pyramid Temple of Tenochtitlán. The place where the priests rip out hearts as soon as look at you. Even down here at the bottom you can see the flame before the altar, lit by sunlight reflected from a pyrites mirror. If you climb up, you're a goner for sure.

All the same, it's up to you. If you want to take the steps to the top of the pyramid, turn to 91. Otherwise return to your map at 19 and select another destination.

32

"Hey, pretty fella," you call out cheerfully. "Nice fella! Good fella! Lovely skunk. Dear sweet little skunkie baby, come over here and let's have a little chat."

The skunk looks over its shoulder at you suspiciously.

Not that you'd blame it. Ever think you'd be standing on top of a Mexican pyramid in the burning sun trying to make friends with a skunk? If you want to go on with this lunacy, turn to 142. Otherwise you still have the option of running at 59 or starting a fight at 98.

You slip through the door and into the sunlight. You can hardly believe it – you're free! But something's wrong. This isn't Tenochtitlán, the bustling Aztec capital you know so well. You are standing among the towering ruins of a city that was ancient when the Aztecs first came to this land.

You look to your left and see, distantly, an enormous stepped pyramid. You look to your right and see another, so gigantic that it dwarfs the first. A half-buried memory stirs. This must be Teotihuacán, the mysterious sacred city the Aztecs call 'The Place of Those Who Have the Road of the Gods'.

Only Aztec priests live here, the same priests who are determined to take your life. And you have no idea at all how to find your way out. Check your immediate surroundings on the map on page 25 and decide where you want to go.

Swiftly you leap forward and slam into the nearest of the five who, to your surprise, falls down as if poleaxed, leaving only four facing you.

"No need to be like that!" one of them exclaims. "We were only making comments. No offence intended."

You step back a pace. "You mean you don't want to fight?"

"Appearances can be very deceptive in a game book," one of them tells you wide-eyed. "I mean I know we all look terribly butch, but the truth is we wouldn't hurt an axolotl fly."

"Or flyolotl, as we call it," says another, "because it flies a lot."

"In fact," says the first, "we surrender. Why don't you just take our arms and equipment and our booty and leave us in peace?" **Wouldn't bet on this happening every time you get into a spot of bother: between them, these goons have five quills of gold dust, 15 tin Ts, a +10 sword, seven +5 arrows, a -5 feather shield, and a container of pulque. Take what you'd like, then go north to 72, east to 84, or through the door to 118.**

MAP OF TEOTIHUACÁN

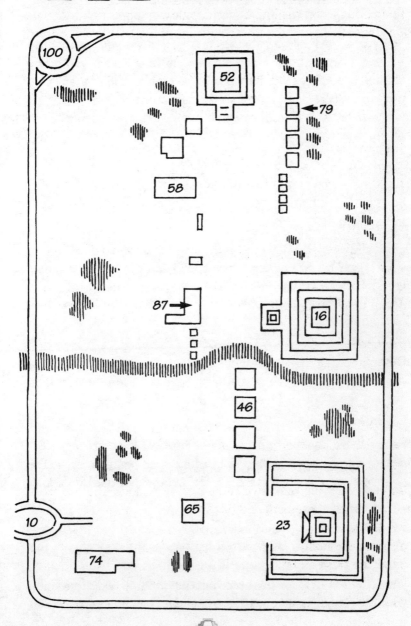

25

35

This climb is harder than it looks – a lot harder. The problem is the terraces are in very bad repair. (In some places the masonry seems to be held together only by creepers and vines.)

You can always climb back down to 52, but if you want to go on, you'd better try an Absolutely Anything Roll. If you make that successfully, you can climb the rest of the way at 5. If not, you MUST climb down to 52, unless of course you manage to kill yourself, in which case you'll just naturally fall all the way to 13.

36

Wow, once you step inside, the pong is positively crucial! What's been going on here? It smells as if two thousand skunks crawled in here and died.

Look, are you ABSOLUTELY sure you don't want to change your mind? If you back out now to 33 you can select a much less smelly destination. But since it's your choice, you can press on regardless to 129.

37

Blow this for a game of soldiers, you've just walked into a brace of hunting jaguars! (Or ocelotls, as we like to call them in this neck of the woods.) They're big, they're black, they're hungry – and one of them just glanced in your direction and licked its lips.

Fancy your chances fighting these brutes? If so, turn to 76. But the good news is they're hunting deer, not you, so you've a chance to run like hell for 33 and pick another destination.

38

You stand watching with mixed feelings as the remnants of the opposing team are marched off for sacrifice, but better them than you. All around the crowd are cheering their heads off, delighted with the slaughter that has already taken place.

Wearily, you begin to make your way off the court. You are mostly just relieved to have escaped this latest adventure, but part of you is thinking about the far flung Aztec Empire, and hoping that the invading Spaniards will somehow manage to overthrow it. But you have doubts. There are so few Spaniards – a few hundred at most – compared to the hundreds of thousands of Aztecs ranged against them. Even with the support of vassal nations like your own, it would be a miracle if they overthrew the mighty Montezuma.

"Well done, young Hummingbird!" exclaims a man in a mask, and you recognise the smooth voice as that of Prince Nezahualcoyotl. "Few times there I thought you'd had it. Still, hard to kill a bad thing, I always say!"

"What do we do now?" you ask, in no mood for his levity.

"Well," says Prince Nezahualcoyotl, "you're free to go now. That's the law. Anybody who survives the game is free to go where they want. If you were a slave, which you aren't, you'd have earned your freedom. If you were a criminal, which you aren't, you'd be pardoned for your crimes. If you were waiting to be sacrificed, which you aren't, you'd still have to be sacrificed for the good of the country and the glory of the gods, but only for that! You're free to go as a slave or a criminal!"

"In that case I'll be off," you tell him quickly.

But Prince Nezahualcoyotl holds up one hand. "One small thing – the Emperor has asked to see you. He thought you played brilliantly, so he graciously extended an invitation for you to have a cup or two of pulque with him in the palace at four. No obligation, of course. The law still says you can go anywhere you want, even if it means ignoring the Emperor. It's just that I need to know your answer so I can tell him in case he wants to have you slaughtered for your cheek. So what do you say?"

Interesting question. As Prince Nezahualcoyotl says, you're free to zip off and take your chances in the city, which you can do at 19. But if you feel it would be better to be polite to the most powerful figure in the whole known universe, you can accept Montezuma's gracious invitation at 62.

It's really stuffy in here, so stuffy your torch is beginning to flicker badly from lack of oxygen. Maybe you should turn back before this starts to do you damage.

To turn back all you have to do is go to 105 and try another exit. But if you insist on going breathlessly where no sacrificial victim has gone before, stumble on to 130.

You've stumbled on the remains of an ancient obsidian workshop!

If there were ever wooden seats here, they're now gone, and even the stone benches are crumbling. But there are lots of signs of what went on here long ago, in the lumps of black, brown and even green volcanic glass strewn around.

Hurriedly you begin to scrabble round in the debris. Obsidian makes marvellous weapons – arrowheads, spearheads, knives. The sacrificial razors used by the Aztec priests are all made from obsidian. If there are any weapons left here in this workshop, they are likely to be better than the ones you're using.

But the big question is can you find them? Roll one die. Score 1, 2 or 3 and your search is fruitless. Score 4 or 5 and you find a +5 obsidian knife. Score 6 and you've hit jackpot with an extra long obsidian blade of the finest quality, which hacks up your enemies at an astonishing +10.

You're only allowed one search, so whatever the result, turn now to 33 and select another destination.

Hey, these are really delicious. The sauce isn't at all sweet and the meat is tasty and tender. What's more, the whole thing's so nourishing it gives you an astounding +10 damage on every blow you land in your next fight.

Talking of which, if you still want to fight the guard, turn to 18. If not, go at once to 68.

There's an ominous rumbling as the great stone tilts forward, threatening to crush you. But then, with a roar of hidden machinery, it withdraws revealing not a secret chamber, but an opening in the floor above a flight of stone steps leading into darkness. The opening is criss-crossed with remarkably fresh-looking spider webs.

Listen, you don't have to go down there you know. There are spiders in these old ruins that could poleaxe a crocodile just by tickling it. Maybe best to get back to 33 and pick another destination.

But if you insist on going down those steps, throw two dice.

Score 2, 3 or 4 and a great hairy spider drops down the inside of your loincloth to poison all your Life Points: go directly to 13.

Score 5, 6 or 7 and the spider gives you a poisoned bite equivalent in damage to a double dice roll multiplied by three. If this kills you, go to 13. If it doesn't, squash the spider against your thigh (yuk!) and descend the steps to 67.

Score 8, 9 or 10 and the spider bites you with damage equivalent to a single die roll multiplied by three. If this kills you, go to 13. If it doesn't, squash the spider against your thigh (yuk again!) and descend the steps to 67.

Score 11 or 12 and you're bitten by the extremely rare cozcaquauhtli spider, whose poison will restore any Life Points you may have lost up to your full maximum and leave you immune to poison for the rest of this adventure. Skip refreshed down the steps to 67.

"Excuse me," you say hesitantly, "but are you one of the wicked Aztec priests who wishes to prematurely end my sweet young life, or are you some innocent stranger who just happens to be sitting in a ruined little pyramid minding his own business?"

"I am some innocent stranger who just happens to be sitting in a ruined little pyramid minding his own business," says the figure sadly, "and you, Señor, have split an infinitive."

The accent tells you at once this is no Aztec priest. You've stumbled on a member of the invading Spanish forces, although what he's doing all the way out here is a mystery.

"Boy, am I glad to see you!" you tell him enthusiastically. "The Aztecs are after me as a human sacrifice!" When he doesn't reply, you add, "You know, the Aztecs. They're the ones you're fighting. The bad guys. Any enemy of theirs has to be a friend of yours – right?"

But the man is slowly shaking his head. "I fear I can be of little help to you, young Señor. I am currently dying from some noxious disease, which I doubtless caught while hacking my way through your ghastly jungles in order to wipe out the Aztec civilization. I have only a few seconds left to live. But you are welcome to all that I have, little though it is." He coughs. "Don't come too close." He coughs again. "I'm afraid my musket has no ammunition."

"Your musket?" you ask, suddenly interested, since a firearm would mean you could take on half a dozen priests with some chance of winning. "Where is your musket?"

"Aaaarrrrgh!" replies the Spaniard.

"Pardon?" you say politely.

But the conversation comes to an abrupt end as the Spaniard falls to the ground. Dead.

All the same, it's an ill wind ... There's a musket lying beside him which would give you +10 damage on a hit if you happened to have any ammunition for it. If you scrabble around, you'll also find three vials of El Gringo brand hair and body tonic, each of which will restore a double dice roll of Life Points.

Finally, if you don't mind robbing a corpse, you can equip yourself with the Spaniard's rather nifty iron breastplate, which will subtract 8 points of damage from any successful blow scored against you in a fight. But be careful not to squeeze his chest when you're taking it off – if this guy breathes on you, you're a goner. Throw one die. Score 3, 4, 5 or 6 and you get the breastplate successfully. Score 1 or 2 and he breathes germs all over you and you go to 13. If you survive, you can return to 33 and select another destination, or investigate the buildings to your right by turning to 37.

This passage is definitely man-made. The floor is flagged all the way and the walls are made from dressed stone. More to the point, you find a small bag of pulque leaves which you can soak in water to make three doses of the intoxicating medicine, each one of which will restore a single die roll of Life Points. And if that wasn't enough, you also find a small portable baked clay tablet which contains a Toltec Death Spell.

Your fifth drink of pulque will always land you at 96. You can find out about the Toltec Death Spell at 144. (Make a note of where you are now before you go.) The passage itself winds like a great serpent all the way to 52.

45

Since there's no time to lose, you move off in the warm velvet darkness. It's impossible to see anything more than a centimetre or so before your face. All around you come the coughs, grunts, screams and cries of wild (and wildly dangerous) animals.

Could be this wasn't such a bright idea after all. If you want to change your mind, there's still time to back out of the jungle, retrace your steps, and march into Tenochtitlán with the Prince and his men at 54. Alternatively you can press on, blind as a bat, in this hostile environment until you come to 99.

46

These four buildings look as if they may once have been small pyramids, but they're now so tumble-down it's difficult to tell. But what you can tell is that there's something coughing in one of the buildings to your right. The trouble is, there's something coughing in one of the buildings to your left as well: the coughs sound horribly like the noise made by a brace of hunting jaguars.

If you'd like to investigate the buildings on your right, turn to 37. If you want to find out what's moving in the buildings on your left, go to 85. If neither of these options appeal, return to 33 and pick another destination.

47

"Hold on!" you exclaim, "I mean no-one any harm. I'm in the Palace by invitation and I can assure you I opened your door purely by mistake and will, if you permit, leave peacefully."

"You'll be so lucky!" growl all five in unison.

You're in trouble, unless you can slam the door before these numskulls fall on you. They're so dumb they'll forget about you the minute you're out of sight. So try an Absolutely Anything Roll. If it fails, the thugs will beat you to a pulp, then deposit your body at 13. But if, as is far more likely, you succeed, then you can get back outside and make the choice of going north to 72, east to 84, or through the doors to 104 and 118.

Hey, looks like you just got lucky. Somebody's been down here before you – and not an Aztec either. There's a small leather pouch of distinctly Spanish design which contains enough powder and shot to make six musket rounds.

You look around for a musket, but there's none to be found, so you hurry onwards … only to walk smack into a blank wall.

Unless you want to search for a secret passage at 111 your only option is to go back to 105 and try another exit.

49

There's a flight of stone steps leading up onto a three-tiered platform, with further steps leading from there to the higher reaches of the pyramid itself.

As you approach, you notice carved onto the surface of the platform a representation of a feathered serpent, and realise this pyramid must be an ancient temple to the creator god Quetzalcóatl.

You smile a little. Just before you were captured, your father told you the Aztecs believe Hernán Cortés, the leader of the invaders from the East, is Quetzalcóatl come again to reclaim his empire. No wonder the Spaniards were doing so well in their battles.

But you have no time to reminisce. The priests may find you at any moment. Swiftly you mount the second flight of steps …

Only to find the entrance to the pyramid closed off by a thick stone slab on which is cut the inscription:

To enter here, quadruple the number of letters in the colour of MALINALLI and go at once to that section.

You stop. Malinalli is an Aztec word, but you're having a little trouble in recalling what it means.

If you know what malinalli means in English, count the number of words in its colour, multiply by four and turn to that section. If you're stuck, your only option is to return to 4.

50

The plaza is one of the few places in the city where you can walk for any distance without falling into a canal. The canals are the public transport system of Tenochtitlán and there's scarcely an Aztec family in the whole city that doesn't own a canoe.

You walk towards the great towering red edifice and stand staring upwards. Although smaller than the Great Temple Pyramid, Montezuma's Palace is not one measure less imposing. The monumental stonework gives it a grandeur, while at the same time its obvious fortifications are a deterrent to attack from those with whom the Emperor is less than popular.

Will you be permitted to enter? You're soon going to find out since there's a heavily armed guard approaching you right now.

"Have you been invited to meet the Angry Lord our Emperor?" he asks abruptly.

Well, have you? If you have, the guard will escort you inside at 24. If not, your only sensible option seems to be to go to 19 and select another destination from the map there.

51

"Take the eastern corridor when you leave the throne room," Montezuma tells you, "at the end you'll see three doors. It's the one on the right that you want. Don't go in either of the other doors," he adds, without explaining why.

"No, sir," you promise, wondering what's behind the other doors.

"You'll have to forgive my not going with you, but I'm a very busy Emperor, organising sacrifices and suchlike."

"I quite understand," you tell him, bowing obsequiously.

Once outside, you find yourself with a choice of two corridors and a door.

The question is, *do* you want to waste time at the Monster Menagerie if you *don't* really have to? The eastern corridor to the menagerie runs to 84, but since Montezuma isn't with you and there's nobody about, what's to stop you taking the northern corridor to 72, or trying the door at 104?

You emerge into the overgrown remains of what was once an open courtyard surrounded on three sides by buildings. To the north rises a great stepped pyramid with what looks like a smaller pyramid actually built onto its southern side. On the top of the larger pyramid stands a rough hewn statue of some elder god who doubtless presided over the life of this ancient city long before the Aztecs marched here all the way from Aztlan.
This is a really creepy place. Not only is there no sign of any of the dreaded Aztec priests, there's no sign of anything. It's deathly quiet. Not a deer, not a coyote, not a rabbit, skunk, puma, bear, armadillo, tapir, monkey or iguana. Not a bird sings, not a parrot, buzzard or sparrow hawk flies. It's as if the place was somehow … waiting.

It's certainly waiting for you to make a move. Which you can do by climbing the terraces of the smaller pyramid at 35, trying to find a way up the larger pyramid at 12, or running like hell back to 33 to pick another destination.

Meditate, meditate, meditate, worry, worry, nervous, need a loo, wonder, speculate, worry, nervous, nervous.

Well, that would seem to be more than enough of that nonsense. Now you've worked yourself up into a right old state of nerves, your only options would appear to be suicide (go to 13) or taking your courage in both hands and stepping through that door to meet the Aztec Emperor, Lord Montezuma, at 78.

The approach to Tenochtitlán is stunning. You, Prince Nezahualcoyotl and his men march along the northernmost of the three causeways that connect the lake city to the mainland. From this Tepeyacac causeway, you can see the two others – the great road west to Tiacopan and the branched causeway south to Ixtapalapa and Coyoacan.

You can also see Xochimilco, the amazing floating garden which produces so much of the city's food. The garden is older by far than the Aztec Empire itself, and is made up of floating rafts covered with rich fertile mud, planted with maize, vegetables and fruit of every description.

Your mind strays onto thoughts of escape: if you could reach Xochimilco, you could live off the fruits that grow there and the big meaty water lizards the Aztecs call axolotls or water dolls. But right now you are surrounded, so you have no option but to continue on into the city.

And what a city it is. The Aztecs built it here because their god told them the place had the same magical properties as their ancient Aztlan homeland. They laid it out in a geometric grid and divided it into four quarters, each with five sub-divisions. But the real division is between Tenochtitlán proper, built around the Great Temple, where Montezuma and the upper classes live, and Tiateloco, home of the lower classes.

Any time you've been here (in the days before your people joined the revolt against the Aztecs) you've only ever dared go into Tiateloco. But now you find Prince Nezahualcoyotl is herding you towards Tenochtitlán proper.

As you march through the milling crowds of people, many of whom turn to stare at you curiously, your eyes slide over several of the city's five hundred stone-built palaces. Their structures are crowned with battlements and ornamented with serpents. You are walked past canals, criss-crossing the city like a shining spider-web. Some poet once described these canals as 'circles of jade, radiating flashes of light like quetzal plumes' – but he wasn't being dragged to a ball game where the losing team is executed.

As you approach the central section of the capital, the land grows less marshy, and the buildings become more substantial. Many of them are pyramid temples with sacrificial fires before their altars. The sight of them reminds you that the priests are still looking for you ...

You reach the Great Temple on the central plaza with its surround of high buildings, which are actually houses of the dead. For one ghastly moment you think Prince Nezahualcoyotl and his men are going to stop here, but they continue until they reach the entrance of a walled stadium.

"We're here," says Prince Nezahualcoyotl. "Want to learn the rules before tomorrow's game?"

If you would like to enjoy the Aztec Deathmatch as an ingenious new board game based on the original cosmic ritual of ancient South America, you'll find full instructions on how to make and play it at section 15. If you can't find a friend to play the game with, or just think making up a board game is too much of a hassle, you can continue with your adventure by plunging into the bloodthirsty version of the game at 17.

55

You finish off the grubs and ants, but push the rest aside. "I think I've had enough," you tell the guard, who bends to pick up your tray.

The guy is ripe for a sucker punch in this position. If you want to start a fight, turn to 18 where you can strike first blow without having to roll for it. Otherwise, turn now to 68.

That's interesting – there's a temple entrance on this level. And by the looks of things, somebody's been doing some clearance work round here quite recently.

Which means you're likely to bump into one or more Aztec nasties if you venture inside at 89, but that's your choice as always. Your other choices include joining up with the zig-zag path to the summit at 77, or climbing back down that rickety ladder (with another Absolutely Anything Roll I'm afraid) and returning to 33 to select another destination.

Most of the passageway is a natural rock fissure, but there are parts where it looks as if somebody has widened things out. One place has definitely been worked either by the Aztecs or earlier builders, because there is stone flagging on the floor and cut stone slabs set into the walls.

At one point you reach what appears to be a cross passage, but investigation quickly shows it's nothing of the sort. Somebody has cut two large, but empty, side chambers off the main passage.

You continue to follow it in a vaguely north-westerly direction until, to your astonishment, it comes to a dead end.

What a waste of time! Unless you want to search for a secret passage at 112, your only option is to go back to 105 and try another exit.

This building looks as if it might have been a treasure house at one time, possibly containing goodies for the nearby Pyramid of the Moon temple. There's a huge stone slab set into one wall that looks as if it's sealing off a special chamber. Carved into the surface of the stone are the words:

PRESS THE JAGUAR TO PASS THE STONE

Sounds like some very obscure medical advice. But directly below the inscription are four symbols labelled:

XOCHITL   ACATL   OCELOTL   MAZATL

The problem is which one to press, a problem made a little more acute by a line of graffiti scrawled in the dirt as if by a dying hand. The graffiti reads:

The stone squashed me because I pressed the wrong one.

But you're not likely to press the wrong one and get squashed, are you? If you press Xochitl go to 63. If you press Acatl go to 29. If you press Ocelotl go to 42. If you press Mazatl go to 2. Of course, you don't have to risk any of this if you don't want to. There's absolutely nothing stopping you returning to 33 and selecting another destination.

Roll two dice as you race blindly hither and yon through this picturesque ruined city.

Score 2, 3 or 4 and end up at 33.

Score 5, 6, 7 or 8 and you end up at 65.

Score 9, 10, 11 or 12 and you end up at 92.

As you clear the soldiers' encampment, you pause to work out a plan of action. If you head back to the road, the chances are you're going to bump into Prince Nezahualcoyotl and the lads sooner or later. But if you stay off the road in the jungle, the chances are you're going to be eaten by a jaguar or poisoned by a rattlesnake sooner or later.

Sometimes life hardly seems worth living. If you want to take your chance in the jungle, turn to 45. If you figure you can avoid Prince Nezahualcoyotl and the lads on the road, go to 81.

61

This may not have been such a good idea. As you scrabble around in the rubble, an ominous noise behind you causes you to freeze. Slowly you look around to find yourself staring into the glittering eyes of a burly Aztec priest. He smiles slowly and draws a wicked knife from his belt.

If this character knows you're supposed to be a ritual sacrifice, it looks like he's decided on a do-it-yourself approach. He has 40 Life Points, two containers of pulque which he'll use if his Life Points drop below 10, and the knife gives him +5 on every hit.

If the priest kills you, go to 13.

If you survive, you can take any pulque he hasn't used. Each dose will restore a die roll of Life Points when you need it, but if it's the fifth container you've used, you must go directly to 96 after you've used it. To make sure you get out of this dangerous place with a whole skin, turn to 33 and select a new destination from the map. Or if you still haven't learned your lesson and insist on continuing your search, try 70.

62

"Well if it's an invitation from the Emperor ... " you begin. But your mind is racing. It was Montezuma who condemned you to die, Montezuma who decided only your sacrifice could stop the invading Spanish. The question is, will he recognise you?

You begin to sweat. Your problem is there's a blank between the time of your capture on the field of battle and your awakening in the Teotihuacán cell. If the Emperor saw you during that time, meeting him now will be a short cut to Section 13.

But if he didn't, where could be safer for you than the Palace? No-one is going to hassle the Emperor's guest.

" ... I suppose I shall have to accept," you tell the Prince with a sickly grin.

"Capital!" exclaims Prince Nezahualcoyotl.

Well, what are you waiting for? On the double to the Emperor's Palace at 50.

Splat! The stone's fallen down and crushed you.

Toss yourself like a pancake to section 13.

This is a fort! The place is crawling with warriors! Sometimes you make the dumbest decisions about your destinations.

There's obviously nothing for you here except to turn, tiptoe away and hope nobody notices you.

You turn, tiptoe away, hoping nobody notices you.

"Scuse me!"

You freeze, then slowly turn. Your blood runs cold. Standing no more than three feet away from you, glaring at you with icy eyes, is the most feared, the most dangerous, the most hated individual in the entire Aztec Empire. More terrible than Montezuma, more horrible than the High Priest, the insignia on his featherwork cloak identifies him beyond all doubt.

You are staring at the dreaded ...

Tax Collector!

"Scuse me," he says again, "but have you filled in this aloe-leaf form in triplicate?"

"Well, no, actually – " you begin.

"And have you forwarded certified returns of income for yourself, your parents and your ancestors for seven generations?"

"Not ... precisely – " you try to tell him, painfully.

"And are you carrying documentation identifying you as a *bona fide* Aztec, or failing that a free citizen of the Aztec Empire, or a native of a vassal nation within the meaning of the Vassal Nations (Sacrifice Fodder) Act of – "

There's only one way to deal with this clown – hit him with everything you've got. He has 50 Life Points, which could be worse, and carries only a small +2 dagger, but if he elects to shower you with official forms (which he'll do every time he makes a score of 10 or better) you'll find half your remaining Life Points disappear through sheer exhaustion. Should the Tax Collector kill you, go in triplicate to 13. If you survive, return to 19 and pay more attention when you're making your next selection.

65

This isolated building doesn't look big enough for a store and is certainly no temple, pyramid or fortress. It is heavily overgrown, but somebody has hacked away the creepers that obscured the open doorway, so it's obviously been in use recently.

A curious and highly unpleasant smell emanates from the dim interior as you approach.

Are you sure you want to go into this pongy old building? You can always change your mind by returning to 33 and selecting a new destination. But if you positively must go ahead, turn to 36.

66

You push open the door. Inside, two feathered warriors spring to their feet and heads turn in your direction. But your attention is locked onto the figure at the far end of this massive chamber.

Although you have never seen him before, not even in a state procession, you know at once this must be the Angry Lord himself, the Emperor of all the Aztecs, First Speaker and former High Priest, Montezuma.

He is seated on a golden throne inlaid with turquoise, a man in his middle years, black haired with a drooping black moustache, and piercing, dark-brown eyes. He is wearing a cotton loincloth and the sort of feathered cloak much favoured by the nobility. On his head is a mitre crown, very similar – if larger and grander

– to the headgear worn by many of the priesthood, except that Montezuma's mitre sparkles with precious stones.

Above him hangs an enormous canopy of featherwork with a gold and jewelled centre. Around him on the walls hang rich tapestries in thread of many colours spun from wild animal hair, interwoven with rings of purest gold.

But for all the grandeur, all the riches, you find your eyes drawn to the stool set before the Emperor. On it is a human skull crowned with an emerald pyramid and a spray of plumes and precious stones. It is the most repulsively fascinating thing you have ever seen.

"Ah," exclaims the Emperor, "the hero of the Cosmic Ball Game has arrived. Approach! Approach!"

Hesitantly you move forward. It seems the Angry Lord has not recognised you as his intended sacrificial victim. At the foot of the throne you bow, mainly to keep your face out of sight.

"Oh, no formalities!" exclaims Montezuma. "I'm so sick of everybody bowing and scraping. Besides, we were just discussing a little problem and I would welcome your input."

"Certainly Your Angryness," you mumble, trying to keep your face in shadow while simultaneously disguising your voice.

"Our problem is this," Montezuma announces grandly. "As you know, our great Empire is currently under attack by invaders from the East. In my wisdom, I decreed that the best way to turn them back was to sacrifice a young prisoner at the holy city of Teotihuacán. But this despicable (and singularly ugly) person has somehow managed to escape. The only alternative I can see is to sacrifice 70,000 prisoners right here in Tenochtitlán."

Seventy thousand sacrifices? You stare at him aghast. But Montezuma doesn't seem to notice and goes on, "The organisational problems are quite large – 70,000 prisoners will make a line some three kilometres long which will have to be guarded; and the actual sacrifices will take days to complete … "

"But, sir – " you begin to protest, appalled.

Montezuma holds up his hand. "I know what you're going to say," he tells you. "There's nothing to beat a good holiday, and if it stops the invaders, why not? My sentiments entirely. But some of my advisers say we should try to find the original sacrifice who escaped, thus saving us a lot of trouble and, incidentally, 69,999 lives. What do you think?"

He leans forward, eager to hear your opinion.

What a wonderful moral dilemma you are presented with. All you have to do is give yourself up now and you will instantly save 69,999 lives. Think about it for a minute, then, if you want to turn yourself in, speak up bravely at 27. If you'd prefer to save your own skin, you'll be a lot safer at 93.

As you step forward, you hear a distant drumming sound, but it turns out to be no more than your heart pounding in your chest. You start down the steep stone steps into darkness.

You count thirteen steps before your feet touch the stone flagged floor at the bottom. You step into the secret chamber and after a while your eyes grow accustomed to the gloom.

At once you wish they hadn't because only a few feet in front of you crouches a huge black jaguar (or ocelotl as you now know it's called.) You leap backwards in panic, scrabbling for a weapon. The great cat doesn't move a muscle.

You retreat up the steps, but halfway up you realise why it hasn't moved – it's a larger than life-size, and very life-like, statue. Sheepishly you climb down again to investigate the chamber.

At first it seems empty except for that life-like statue, but then you notice something beneath one of the jaguar's paws. Gingerly you ease it out and discover it's a rolled manuscript. But it's not made from aloe leaf paper like most Aztec manuscripts. This one is made from silk, treated with a special gum to give it extra strength and make it last.

Excitedly you carry the manuscript back up to the light.

And well might you feel excited, because what you've got there is an ancient Toltec Ocelotl Prayer. This prayer has such a soothing effect on all the great cats (and most of the little ones) that they will positively refuse to attack you no matter what. Roll one die to find out how often you can use the prayer before the silken paper crumbles into dust, then move happily back to 33 to select another destination.

The guard leaves, carefully closing the door behind him. But he seems a little awkward because of the tray, and now he's gone you notice a chink of light to one side of the door. Breathlessly you investigate. To your delight, the door has not been properly fastened from the outside. You wait a little to make sure the guard has gone, then put your shoulder to the door and push.

This may be good news. Turn to 33 to find out.

You hurl yourself upon the hunched-up figure and strike. Then you realise at once he's not an Aztec priest. This is one of the Spanish invaders, the people you're supposed to be helping to overthrow the Aztec tyranny. He coughs in your face as you hurriedly extricate yourself, groans once then falls to the ground dead.

This is a bigger mess than you think. The Spaniard was coughing because he had one of those terrifying diseases from the Old World, against which native South Americans like you have no immunity. What's more, he coughed in your face before you killed him. I could tell you how your body temperature rises to about 40 °C, or how the lymph nodes in your groin, thighs and armpits grow to the size of footballs and become filled with pus, infecting your bloodstream, so the disease rages through your body causing you to die in agony. But why not spare yourself all that by going directly to 13?

By Mayahuel (a pulque goddess) you've found something! You can see the faintest gleam of reflected light beneath a broken slab. Hurriedly you rip it up and discover underneath a wonderfully carved quartz crystal skull.

Could come in useful! But now you're pushing your luck staying here. Turn quickly to 33 and select a new destination.

Darkness. Your head hurts as if somebody just bashed it with a club. Which, now you come to think of it, was exactly what happened.

For a moment you more than half believe you're back in Section 1, but when you open your eyes you find yourself in bright sunlight tied to an altar on the top of the Pyramid of the Sun at Teotihuacán. Looming over you is the tall, slim figure of the High Priest in loincloth and cloak, with an elaborate feathered head-dress in imitation of the creator god Quetzalcóatl. He is holding a ceramic bowl in one hand and a long obsidian blade in the other. His cohorts are standing around him grinning evilly.

"Why are you doing this?" you gasp.

To your surprise, the High Priest answers soberly. "Because Montezuma, the Angry Lord, has ordered it."

"But why just me and why here?" you wail.

"An intelligent question. What with the Tlaxcalan revolt and the Spanish invasion (which we believe to be the return of Quetzalcóatl, of course) this has been a *dreadful* year. You'd imagine we'd want to sacrifice half the population. But our Emperor, in his wisdom, believes just one small Tlaxcalan sacrifice will be enough, provided it's carried out here."

"Why here?" you ask, still trying to put off the evil moment.

"Because this is Teotihuacán, and Teotihuacán was built by the mighty Toltecs more than a thousand years before my people ever colonised this land," says the High Priest. "This is a holy city of great magical power. A single sacrifice here is worth a million slaughtered somewhere else, or so Montezuma believes. But enough of the chatter," he says, suddenly serious, "Are you ready to have your beating heart ripped from your breast and placed in this bowl, so Quetzalcóatl will turn the Spaniards back?"

"No!" you say firmly.

But the high priest ignores you.

Go to 13 and regrow your heart.

This was not a good choice. Before you've gone two dozen paces, the twists and turns of this corridor have you hopelessly lost. It's like walking through a maze and the further you go, the more confused you get.

You turn back, but soon find that's even worse. Without a guide to help you, this place is an absolute nightmare. What's more, you're beginning to feel both tired and hungry.

Start

Out

Sometimes things just don't turn out the way you want. But there's hope. Sooner or later you'll find your way out of this maze. The real problem is how long it will take you. Time yourself as you tackle the maze and deduct one Life Point for every minute it takes you to get from the point marked IN to the point marked OUT. If this kills you, go to 13. If you survive, you'll find yourself back where you can take the corridor north to 72, the corridor east to 84, or the doors to 104 or 118.

Hey, wow, this is really neat! The crystal skull fits the indentation like a hand sliding into a well-oiled glove. And as it does so, you hear a distinct click and the whole surface slab of the altar moves sideways a little.

Excitedly you push the slab further and it slides to reveal the interior of the altar. You fumble inside, but pull your hand out with a yelp due to the bird-eating spider hanging on your finger!

Which fortunately isn't poisonous! Throw the arachnid away and you'll find a small locked golden casket inside the altar. You'll also find a thin stone tablet inscribed with the Aztec characters for SPECIAL PASS. LET THE BEARER THROUGH OR SUFFER MONTEZUMA'S REVENGE. SIGNED MONTEZUMA. This could come in useful. And even though you can't open the casket, it looks valuable. So you take them both and return to 33 to pick another destination.

Heaven only knows what this building was used for. It's so broken down you'd have trouble telling whether it was a laundry or a library. But your search is rewarded with a container of pulque (which will restore a die roll of Life Points when you need it, but if it's the fifth container you've used, you must go directly to 96 after you've used it) and an inscribed stone plaque.

The inscription is in Nahuatl, the language of the Aztecs, and though you speak it fluently, you have problems reading it. You make out the pictograph characters for ozomatl (monkey), cipactli (crocodile), malinalli (grass), atl (rain or water), itzcuintli (dog) and miquiztli (skull or death). Does the story read: 'That cheeky monkey of a crocodile came out of the water onto the grass and ate my dog'? Or 'A monkey watched while my dog jumped from the grass to the water and killed a crocodile'? You decide you may never know and leave this ruin, clutching your container of pulque.

Return to 33 and select another destination from the map.

You journey down the road only to reach a fork in it blocked by thirty hairy Aztec warriors. The chief of this heavy-duty pack eyes you suspiciously.

"Leaving the city is it?" he asks.

"Could be," you say cautiously.

"Not today you aren't," he tells you grimly. "All roads out are blocked on account of some young foreign scum who had the cheek to run away just because our holy priests were going to cut his heart out in Teotihuacán? Seen anybody like that, have you?"

"No," you say quickly, "no indeed. Absolutely, positively not."

"Never mind," the guard remarks menacingly. "We'll get the little bleeder, don't you fret. We've men looking for him all over the city." He sniffs. "Now where did you say you were headed?"

"Just going back to the temple to say a few prayers," you say.

And head back, whistling innocently, to 19 where you can pick another destination.

What a brave little sacrificial victim you are! The animals have 35 Life Points each and attack at +5 on account of vicious teeth and claws. Nonetheless, you hurl yourself fearlessly upon them.

If the jaguars eat you for dinner, go to 13. Should you find you survive this foolhardy venture, turn to 94.

This is exhausting, but the view is great. By the time you're half way up, you can see right across the ruins of the entire city.

As you near the top, you catch a glimpse of a distant roadway to the south west which seems to be leading out of the city in the right direction to take you home. It's such an exciting prospect you can hardly take your eyes off it.

Which probably explains why you didn't notice the Aztec High Priest waiting for you on the platform at the pyramid's summit.

"The gods are kind," he murmurs. "They have brought my Hummingbird to me."

He walks towards you, a long-bladed obsidian knife in his hand.

There's no escaping this nightmare, so you're just going to have to fight him. He has the maximum of 60 Life Points on account of keeping in with the gods, and that knife he carries inflicts +8 damage. If you survive this unfortunate encounter, celebrate at 97. If not, you can frolic all the way to 13.

"You coming?" you ask the guard.

He shakes his head vigorously. "Not me! Nobody in their right mind meets the Angry Lord more than they can help. Too likely to find themselves sacrificed. You're on your own from now on."

"But how do I find my way out when he's finished with me?"

The guard smiles bleakly. "That may not be a problem."

You stare at the door before you. It will, of course, be unlocked since theft is virtually unknown throughout the Aztec Empire, and the only secure chambers are those that hold prisoners.

You lick your lips. You say a silent prayer, then close your eyes in panic, and reach out to push the door ...

Make an Absolutely Anything Roll to find out whether you make it through that door. If the roll shows you die, then you have a heart attack and you stagger off to 13. If you survive, hold your head high and step into 66.

This group of buildings is so overgrown you'd imagine the Aztec priests (or anybody else for that matter) haven't been here for a century or more. As against that, somebody in there seems to be playing the maracas softly to themselves.

If you feel like investigating these musical sounds, turn to 123. If not, there's absolutely nothing stopping you going back to 33 to pick another destination.

80

"That's expensive gear you're wearing," you say slyly. "I expect you're carrying quite a lot of gold as well – gold that you obtained by exploitation of the masses."

"Never!" the man exclaims, shocked.

"A likely story!" you exclaim. And with cries of "Capitalist pig! Exploiter of the masses! Workers of the world unite!" you hurl yourself upon him.

Unfortunately this guy is a lot tougher than he looks. A secret brew of fermented cactus has given him 90 Life Points, and while his ceremonial dagger only gives +2 on hits, he is so skilled with the diplomatic dice that all his scores are doubled. If this ill-considered attack leads to your demise go to 13. If you somehow survive, you can take his +2 ceremonial dagger and return to 33 to select another destination.

81

You wait until dawn, then listen to the consternation as Prince Nezahualcoyotl and his men discover you're missing. You hear them mount a search, but you cunningly shin up a cactus.

You finally hear the Prince call off the search, then the sound of feet marching away. You drop down from the cactus and remove eighty-seven spines from your loincloth. Then you troll off gaily back onto the road that leads to freedom.

"Where do you think you're going, Sunshine?" asks the old familiar voice.

The Foxy Prince had laid in wait with half his men, sending the others down the road as a decoy. You smile weakly as they take your arms and march you to your destiny at 54.

It doesn't lead outside but takes you into a passageway between the inner and outer walls. It's clear this place hasn't been used for a while. You find to your delight five jars of pulque, the fermented juice of the maguey plant, each of which will restore a die roll of Life Points. But once you drink the fifth cup you must go directly to section 96 from wherever you happen to be.

Meanwhile, if you haven't drunk the fifth cup, the only exit from this passage is back the way you came at 4.

"Sorry," you call back cautiously. "I'm afraid I have more serious matters on my mind than silly games."

But you're in trouble. Stepping onto the road is one of the toughest looking Aztec warriors you've seen. Not for him the coarse white nequen fabric made from aloe thread that marks an inferior soldier. Not for him the vest of quilted cotton which the middle rank of warriors wear. This warrior wears a cuirass of gold and silver plate and a surcoat of featherwork. His helmet is shaped as a jaguar, topped by a gorgeous plume. He also wears a collar, bracelets and earrings of gold inlaid with precious stones.

He swaggers towards you. "I'm talking big time here. The roar of the crowd. Your own Talk Show when TV gets invented. And my fee's only ten per cent after deduction of expenses."

You reach for a weapon.

He looks pained. "How come you're making this so difficult? What's wrong with stacking up some gold when you're young?"

But you do not change your mind. You fling yourself upon him, dice rattling, in an attempt to get in the first attack. At which point a squad of fifty heavily-armed soldiers steps onto the road behind him …

This is not good news! If you feel like fighting fifty-one élite Aztec warriors, each one carrying +10 swords, +10 spears and +10 bows with 51 +10 arrows and wearing armour that deducts 20 from every blow scored against them, then be my guest – I'll see you later in 13. On the other hand, if you think there's a case to be made for a strategic surrender, turn to 11.

The walls of the corridor are hung with tapestries of human sacrifice. You wonder how the Aztecs became so bloodthirsty. There's a tradition that they were quite decent up to about two hundred years ago, when they introduced sacrifice into their religion. It is said they were afraid of the end of the world and sacrificed people in order to stop it happening.

You push these thoughts aside as the tapestries begin to feature exotic animals – a development you take to mean you are approaching the Monster Menagerie. And sure enough, a minute or two later, you reach the three doors Montezuma mentioned.

The door on the left leads to 107. The door in the middle leads to 121. The door on the right leads to 136.

Cautiously you enter the ruin, moving silently towards the source of the sound. In the gloom inside the ruin a hunched figure is seated on a stone coughing quietly. This could be one of the priests who are trying to kill you, but it's difficult to be sure in this light.

All the same, if you attack now while he's not looking you can get in the first blow without having to roll the dice for it. You can hurl yourself silently on the coughing figure at 69. If you'd prefer a cosy little chat, which could give him the opportunity of slicing your head off, turn to 43. Should you find it a real killer to have to make up your mind about stuff like this, you can always sneak back quietly to 33 and select another destination.

You can try, but will you succeed?

Only an Absolutely Anything Roll will decide this. If you succeed, you've a choice of going north to 72, east to 84, or through the doors to 104 or 118. If you fail, it's 13, 13, or 13 ...

This used to be a store. Maybe not back in Toltec times, but the Aztecs have certainly been using it as a store recently. There's even an aloe-leaf paper list of contents pinned to the door.

Your eyes widen as you read the list:

Cotton dresses, 10
Featherwork mantles, 8
Ornamental armour, assorted
Vases, 17
Plates, 22, Crystal, 1
Rock, 1, Scroll, 1
Amber, assorted, Jars, 78
Utensils, copper, 16

And on and on. Lots of things you'd really like to have – especially the Scroll. Swiftly you push through the door.

What a swiz! Somebody's been here before you and looted almost everything. About the only thing of any value left is a battered piece of ornamental gold plate armour. The only trouble is there's a rattler curled asleep on top of it ...

So, what are you going to do? If you want that armour you're going to have to tackle the rattler, which you can attempt at 9. If not, back out slowly to 33 and pick another destination.

There's lucky, you've just found a container of pulque! Somebody must have dropped it, which isn't surprising since this is the busiest road in the whole of Tenochtitlán and the favourite of the trading caravans.

Perhaps the find is an omen. You hurry along until you come in sight of the fortified guard post that spans the road as it joins the causeway across the Lake of the Moon onto the mainland.

Omen or not, there's a long queue from the guard post. You join the end and casually ask an elderly Aztec merchant what the problem is. He shrugs. "They're checking everybody. Looking for an escaped prisoner. Want to buy something while you wait? I've got pulque, armour or weapons if you're interested."

There's no question of going on. But are you interested in the merchant's offer? If you want to buy, turn to 101. If not, it's back to the map at 19, but don't forget to roll one die to find out how many doses are in the jar of pulque you found on the road. Each dose restores a die roll of Life Points, but on your fifth dose you must visit 96 after noting your current section.

Gloomy in here. Very gloomy. You fumble your way forward. Around you, you can just make out the looming shapes of huge stone statues, their faces menacing. You fumble a little further forward. As you move from the entrance, the temple gets darker.

Do you want to keep fumbling in the dark? There could be a thousand Aztec priests in here and you wouldn't see them until you walked onto their knives. If you want to keep fumbling, go to 3. If you're having second thoughts, this is your chance – possibly your last chance – to get out to 56.

Even after years of weathering and vegetation attack, even in its crumbling state half-buried in the earth, the great Pyramid of the Sun still manages to look more impressive than any structure in the Aztec capital. The old Toltecs really were master builders, and you find yourself wondering where they learned their skills. Not that wondering will do you any good since nobody now knows where the Toltecs came from or what happened to them after they established this once-great city.

You stare upwards. The pyramid rises in six stages to a final platform at the top. A zig-zag path leads to the summit. On the northern, eastern and southern sides there is a huge platform some forty metres by six, accessed by a crude wooden ladder.

You can climb the pathway at 77 or shin up the ladder at 56. But the ladder's so rickety you'll need an Absolutely Anything Roll to make sure you get up it safely.

If common sense gets the better of you for a change, you can return to 33 and select another destination.

Although not quite so high as the Pyramid of the Sun at Teotihuacán, the Great Temple Pyramid of Tenochtitlán is almost as impressive. Tier after tier of terraces rise up to the platform at the top. This huge construction was made from earth faced with brick, so it may not last as long as the stone built constructions of an earlier age, but it will last long enough.

You climb flight after flight of steps, winding around each tier of the pyramid to do so. So far your luck is holding.

Eventually you reach the top. From the flat platform rise two towers, each around fifteen metres high. Within them are the great stone idols long worshipped by the Aztecs.

Before the towers stands the thing that haunts your dreams, the stone of sacrifice, set between two high altars. For two hundred years now, the Aztecs have sacrificed humans, and you are very much aware you are marked as their next victim.

You shiver and the compulsion that brought you here suddenly breaks. You turn to go. And walk headlong into three priests!

At least it's only half the usual sacrificial complement of six. But that's the only good news. Each of these bruisers carries 45 Life Points and a +5 sacrificial knife, which makes them formidable opponents even though their only garments are the priestly loin cloths and featherwork cloaks that are useless as armour.

You have two choices here – fight or run. But before you can run, you'll have to make an Absolutely Anything Roll to find out if you get past them. If you die in the attempt, go to 13. If you make it past them, run to 19 and select another destination.

If you decide to fight (or, if you fail to run on your Absolutely Anything Roll) and you manage to kill all three priests, you're free to return to 19.

If the priests kill you, go battered and bruised to 13. But these priests, like most Aztecs, will try to capture you alive. They'll manage this if they bring your Life Points below 10 but above 1. Should the priests capture you in this way, turn to 21.

Most of this row of ancient buildings is tumble-down, but the one nearest you seems for some reason to be almost intact. It's overgrown, of course, like almost everything in this ruined city, but the basic structure looks surprisingly sound.

What's even more surprising is that there's no sign the Aztecs have been here, at least not lately. You're cautious, but curious, and you make your way slowly to an opening that looks like the main entrance. There's no sound from within so you slip inside.

Within minutes you discover you haven't entered a primitive house, despite its age, but something far more like an apartment compound. Rooms lead off one another like a maze. The rooms themselves are mostly small – two metres square and two metres by four seem popular sizes – although you do come on one or two that are much larger, as if they were family apartments or communal kitchens.

You come across several other interesting items as well. In several rooms there are sculptures of rabbits, of all things, and scrabbling round in the debris on the floor of a little corridor you find dozens of rabbit bones. Maybe the people who lived here worshipped rabbits. Or, more likely, raised them for food.
As you move further through the maze, you discover it's a virtual treasure trove of absolutely useless items. There are literally

scores of rather well-made little clay figurines, a few very ancient (and unfortunately broken) weapons: clear signs that several families once lived here.

And died here too by the looks of the burial remains, at one time under the floor, but now pushed back to the surface by some long-forgotten earthquake.

This place is quite exceptional, quite unlike your own rather primitive home, and even unlike the best class of Aztec housing. You pop a figurine into your tote bag as a souvenir and turn to make your way out again.

But this building is like a maze! Throw two dice. Score 2, 3 or 4 and you find your way to 33 where you can choose another destination. Score 5, 6 or 7 and you land, in a muddle, at 40. Score anything higher and you lose 3 Life Points. If this kills you, stagger to 13. If not, count yourself lucky at 33.

93

"I'd kill the lot of them," you mutter darkly, allowing yourself only the mental reservation that if the rebellion succeeds, it will stop such slaughter in the future.

"Capital!" exclaims Montezuma delightedly. "Someone after my own heart!" He rounds on his courtiers. "Hear that, you wimps? Hear what the hero of the ball game says? More sacrifices. Tens of thousands more. This hero wants blood by the gallon."

"Well, I didn't exactly say that ... " you protest weakly.

Montezuma ignores you. "Would you like to see my monsters?"

You blink. "Monsters?"

"I keep a menagerie of monsters as well as of animals," Montezuma says. "Most visitors like to see it. Would you?"

Slightly less tricky moral choice here! If you want to visit the menagerie you'll find it at 51. If you don't, turn to 30 instead.

94

How about that? Bruised, bleeding, but unbowed, you place a foot on the prostrate bodies of the two great vicious cats. You open your mouth to vent a triumphant war cry but, because you don't want to be heard, give a triumphant war whisper instead.

You suddenly notice a bag made from the tough canvas cloth you've seen the invading Spaniards use. You look inside. It is packed with enough powder and shot for eighteen rounds. There are also four enormous pills in a package marked *Compounded by Señor Diego de Landa of Calderones, Apothecary to the Royal Stables of His Majestic Emperor Charles V of Spain and France.* They look even more lethal than the shot.

Lucky, especially if you happen to have a musket. And those horse pills are good news if you can force them down. Each one restores a double dice roll of Life Points. Now turn to 33 and select another destination or, if you wish to investigate the coughing noises in the buildings on your left, turn to 85.

This is looking good. The road is straight and true like all major Aztec roads. You can almost smell freedom at the end of it.

Except that up ahead you can see a large crowd of people moving down the road towards you. As they approach you can hear them muttering angrily to one another.

"What's going on?" you ask as the crowd approaches.

"No use going up there," a long-haired woman calls to you sourly. "They've got the army out turning people back. A mosquito couldn't squeeze through on this road."

"But why?" you say, although you've got a pretty good idea.

"Search me," shrugs the woman.

On which unhelpful note you've no option but to return to the map at 19 and select another destination.

You're feeling good. Very good. You're feeling so good you start to dance. You suddenly remember that the hated Aztecs always reserve the fifth cup of pulque for the priests and now you know why. This is really marvellous. You're whirling. You're singing.

Hey, wait a minute, you're blacking out!

Roll two dice. Score 2, 3 or 4 and you wake up at 16. Score 5, 6 or 7 and you wake up at 10. Score 8, 9 or 10 and you wake up with a fearsome hangover and a severe dose of amnesia at 1. Score 11 or 12 and you wake up back at the section where you drank the pulque having mysteriously acquired a sealed vessel containing one dose of foaming cacao which will restore your Life Points to their maximum when you chose to drink it.

With the High Priest out of the way, you move across to the altar, a waist-high stone table with a lot of interesting stains. At one end there's a curious indentation about the size of your head, but you can't for the life of you figure out what it was used for.

You are turning away when you notice an Aztec inscription on the side of the altar. The glyph miquiztli catches your attention.

At first you assume this just describes the sacrificial stone since 'miquiztli' means 'death'. But 'miquiztli' literally means 'skull'. Suddenly the whole inscription becomes clear. It reads:

Place skull in hole on altar.

Frowning, you wonder what you should do.

Actually, there are a limited number of things you can do. If you want to stick your head in that indentation on the altar, go to 119. If you have some other sort of suitable skull, turn to 73. Failing that, your only other option is to go back down the pyramid to 33 and pick another destination.

You leap with mad abandon on the animal, which immediately reaches for its dice to roll for first strike.

If you get first strike and manage to kill the skunk before it gets to hit back, you have a three way choice of going into the larger pyramid at 137, climbing the steps to its top at 155, or climbing all the way back down to 52.

But if the skunk gets first strike, or manages to get in even just one strike before you slaughter the poor little thing, then you're going to smell worse than an Aztec's armpit for the rest of your adventure. You will also have to cope with the immediate effects: roll two dice.

Score 2 and the smell kills you and you go to 13. Score 3 – 6 and you stagger blindly to 23. Score 7 – 9 and you stagger blindly to 65. Score 10 – 12 and you stagger blindly to 79.

The jungle has now become so dense you are no longer able to stand, but you bravely crawl onwards in the darkness as the rustle, coughs and growls of the beasts come nearer. The forest floor beneath your knees becomes suddenly yielding.

And no wonder, since you've just crawled onto the camouflaged cover of a gigantic trap dug by the Aztecs in order to capture animals for food. Suddenly the frail twigs of the cover snap. For just the barest moment time stands suspended and you hang in mid-air. Then you plunge downwards into the trap.

And onto six sharpened upright stakes painted with the most virulent nerve poison known to man. There is a ghastly squelching noise as the spikes penetrate your soft young body, leaving you time only to wriggle round a bit before departing this mortal coil for the waiting arms of Section 13.

Everybody talks about the marvellous road system the Toltecs built – as good if not better than the great Aztec highways. Overgrown as it is, this looks like an ancient Toltec roundabout.

You look at the crumbling paving as boredom starts to eat up through your feet, then turn in the direction of Section 33 hoping that your next choice will be more interesting. But suddenly ...

A dark but very well-dressed figure leaps from the bushes. "Keep away from me!" he yells. "I'm on a road!"

As you stare at this figure a couple of things occur to you. First, he doesn't look Aztec, which is a relief, and secondly his featherwork mantle and cotton kilt are the finest quality. This is somebody of wealth and importance, however nervous he seems.

You hold up both hands. "Calm down," you say politely, "you have nothing to fear from me. Unless, of course, you attack."

"I don't want to attack anybody," the man cries. "I'm an Ambassador!"

So that's it! As an Ambassador from one of the many vassal nations in the Aztec Empire, this man's safety would be absolutely guaranteed by the Aztec authorities. He would be treated with respect, and generally protected.

But only if he stayed on the main highways.

Once he strayed off the highways, all his privileges were lost and he became a target for anybody who felt like beating up a foreigner. No wonder he was nervous. Out here he was miles from the main highways. He was obviously completely lost.

You've a few choices here. Since he's lost, helpless, unprotected and maybe even unarmed, you can beat him up at 80. Or you can decide he's none of your business and simply slip away to 33 where you may select another destination. Or you can take pity on him and try to help at 125.

The merchant unrolls his pack on the ground and spreads out a selection of goods. "All good gear going cheap," he says. "See anything you fancy?"

On the ground are the following items at the following prices: +5 sword @ 1 quill of gold dust; +10 javelin @ 5 quills of gold dust; Container of pulque (6 doses) @ 5 tin Ts; Quiver of arrows (6) @ 1 quill of gold dust; Toltec Death Spell @ 10 quills of gold dust (See 144 if you buy it); Figurine of Quetzalcóatl @ 4 tin Ts; -5 quilted cotton armour vest @ 3 quills of gold dust; Soapstone frog @ 5 cacao beans.

Now carry your booty to 19 and select another destination.

This is the life! The birds are singing, the sun is shining. You have escaped the ghastly ministrations of the Aztec priests.

If Emperor Montezuma thought the only way to stop the Spaniards was a special sacrifice at Teotihuacán, then maybe your escape means the Spaniards are going to win.

Your friend Xolotl is a bit wary of the Spaniards. He thinks the white men are too bloodthirsty for comfort. But surely nothing could be worse than the Aztecs. Their Empire now stretches across a vast swathe of South America, and they keep going to war not to win new territory, but to take prisoners. They never kill an enemy if they can help it. Instead they haul him back to their ghastly capital for sacrifice.

There are six hundred pyramid temples in that blood-soaked city, and every one has its well-used sacrificial altar. However bad the Spaniards may be, they simply can't match that.

Despite these gloomy thoughts, you find your feet taking little skips. You haven't felt this good since you overdosed on pulque. You're going home! You're going home! You're –

"Where do you think you're going, Sunshine?" asks a mellow voice out of the undergrowth beside the road.

You swing round, ready to defend yourself against all comers. "Who is it?" you call. "What do you want of me?"

A throaty chuckle emerges from the jungle. "I'm a talent scout," the voice says. "I want to turn you into a ball game star!"

It's an unusual offer in a place like this, but it doesn't sound such a bad deal. If you'd like to go willingly with the talent scout, turn to 159. If you'd as soon be boiled in oil then go to 83. If you'd like a few more details on his offer, try 8.

103

This broad straight highway joins with a causeway to the mainland and will take you swiftly from this accursed city across the Lake of the Moon and off to freedom.

You move along it trying to avoid drawing attention to yourself. But as the causeway comes into sight, you see a road block manned by more than twenty heavily-armed Aztec warriors.

There's no fighting this many. You might try talking your way past the block at 120, but otherwise it's back to the map at 19 to pick another destination.

You know you've made a mistake the minute you push open the door. There are five members of the imperial guard in here, big, tough, paranoid muscle-men.

"An assassin!" one screams.

"A rebel!" shouts another.

"A threat to our beloved Emperor," yells a third.

The other two just grunt threateningly.

Now the thing is you surprised them, so you can get in the first blow at 34. Or you can use the time to explain you're here at the Emperor's invitation at 47. Alternatively you can try running like crazy at 86.

You're in a subterranean chamber lit by torches set into the walls. The chamber itself is roughly circular, about eight metres wide, with five gloomy exit tunnels. You look up, but find there's no way of climbing back into the shaft through which you fell.

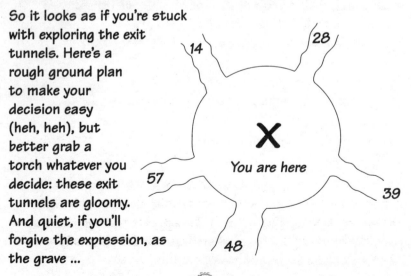

So it looks as if you're stuck with exploring the exit tunnels. Here's a rough ground plan to make your decision easy (heh, heh), but better grab a torch whatever you decide: these exit tunnels are gloomy. And quiet, if you'll forgive the expression, as the grave ...

14

28

X

You are here

57

39

48

106

It's an ill wind, even in the hot and humid season. Now you've dispatched the rattler you can milk its poison sac to make yourself an antidote to any poison you might happen to take in the future. This won't restore lost Life Points, but it will absolutely neutralise poison of any sort, so you can continue with your adventure as if the poisoning had never happened.

Roll one die to discover how many doses of antidote you make, then slither off to 33 to pick another destination.

107

You step inside and find yourself in what looks like Montezuma's private study. On the wall is a tapestry showing an Aztec calendar with special glyphs depicting the five day week, the twenty day month and the eighteen month year.

Below it on a table is a scrap of paper on which somebody has written:

> *The password is Coatlicue.*
> *(Huitzilopochtli is the God of War.)*

Interesting should you need a password, but all you can do now is go back to the corridor where you can choose the door in the middle to 121, the door on the right to 136, or return back up the corridor to the point where you join with the corridor running north to 72 and the door opening into 104.

108

You lift the little document from the casket and discover you're holding in your trembling hands a book of Toltec Death Spells!

To find out about your typical Toltec Death Spell, make a note of the section you're now in, then turn to section 144. When you come back, you'll be pleased to discover the book contains a single die roll of usable spells which may be of benefit when you return, now, to get on with your fight at 156.

To your surprise, the guard smiles as you approach.

"Welcome, pilgrim, to the temple of Quetzalcóatl" he calls cheerfully. "I can't tell you how pleased we are to see you!"

With which he ushers you quickly through the door and closes it.

You look around. The chamber has no windows, but it is brightly lit by a series of flaming torches. In the middle of the floor is a little flat-topped pyramid across which is stretched the body of a frightened boy, held down in the traditional fashion by five priests, one at each of his arms and legs, the fifth at his head. Looming over him is a sixth priest with an sacrificial knife and a big grin on his face.

The priest with the knife catches sight of you. "Welcome, pilgrim," he calls. "How well timed – we're giving this lad to the gods as a sweetener in case they're worried about our sins."

You realise at once where you are. You've stumbled on the Sunday Service in Montezuma's private chapel.

But the point is, what are you going to do about it? If you attempt to save this boy, the likelihood is the priests will kill you, although you can certainly try at 133. But since you're in a big hurry to save your parents, you could duck back out again and try one of the other three doors at 128, 140, or 156.

"I won't be stopped by a couple of flea-bitten Aztecs," you cry.

"Help!" screams one guard.

"Help!" screams the other.

"Help!" scream both guards in unison.

At which point 7,000 heavily-armed reinforcements come charging out of nowhere to their aid.

Each of your 7,002 opponents has 50 Life Points and carries a +5 sword. But the good news is you automatically get in the first strike. When the fight is finished, please go to 13.

Nope, nothing here.

Only thing you can do at this point is to get back to 105 and try somewhere else.

Try an Absolutely Anything Roll, but ignore any score of 2, since even you couldn't manage to kill yourself simply looking for something.

If you get lucky with your Absolutely Anything Roll, you'll find a secret passage at 44. Even if you don't, it was still worth looking because you notice a chink of light marking an exit passage to 16. If you don't fancy either, you can go back to 105 and try another exit.

You close the door carefully behind you so you (hopefully) won't be disturbed, and begin methodically to search the room.

At least until the snake slithers out from behind a box and strikes at you.

No wonder the old boy told you to keep out! You're into a fight now and no mistake, but since the snake surprised you, it automatically gets in the first hit. If this kills you, go to 13. If it doesn't, you'll need to know that the snake has 30 Life Points, and only a mild poison which enables it to strike at +4, but doesn't leave you permanently poisoned. Should this wimpish creature kill you, hang your head and go to 13. But if you survive the attack, you can finish your search at 141.

Nope, nothing here.

Which leaves you with nowhere to go except outside where you have the choice of trying one of the other three doors at 109, 128 or 156.

You gaze at the youth with every indication of rapt attention while your mind considers a dozen different plans.

The youth continues, "I have been chosen by Montezuma and the Aztec priests to play the part of Tezcatlipoca for one year."

You blink. Suddenly this sounds a lot less of a fantasy.

"During the year," the youth continues, "I am treated as a god. I have my own little colony of worshippers. These four beautiful girls are with me at all times. I am fed the best of food – rats in chocolate sauce as often as I want them. I am bathed, sung to, entertained, amused, all my needs cared for …"

"Sounds good," you comment. "Any other jobs going like that?"

"You wouldn't want one," the youth shakes his head sadly. "At the end of the year there is a change of circumstance. I am to be stripped of my finery," he says. "My entourage leaves me and I am taken across the lake to a pyramid temple on the edge of the city. Six priests meet me at the top and conduct me to a massive block of jasper. There five hold me down in the traditional fashion while the sixth, in a scarlet mantle, cuts open my chest with his itztli, or obsidian knife, and removes my heart. After that, they will eat my body at a banquet."

"Wow, heavy!" you exclaim.

"But the worst is, my year's up tomorrow! You must help me!"

"But how can I help?" you ask.

Tezcatlipoca nods to his guards. "I'm afraid you'll have to fight them to release me."

The two large guards step forward and grin at you broadly. One has a gold tooth that glints menacingly in the light.

You realise this guy's problems are none of your business, don't you? A sensible answer might be to decline politely and sidle off to try your luck through one of the other doors to 109, 128 or 156. But if you're mad enough to want to tackle those guards, you can do so at 131.

The pong grows stronger as you tear down this huge heap of skulls in your frantic search.

Ping! goes another Life Point. Ping! then another and another.

As you pick up yet another skull, something about its weight makes you pause and as you examine it closely, you discover it's not a real skull at all, but a cunningly worked ceramic. You turn it over and find it's actually a container.

And a container of alcohol-free pulque, at that. This rare liquid has all the medicinal properties of normal pulque, but since the alcohol has been removed, you can drink as much of it as you like without having to worry about the Fifth Cup Effect. Throw two dice to discover how many doses it contains. As you take each one, throw two dice to discover how many Life Points it restores. Now take your skull and head back out again so you can select another door from 109, 140, or 156.

As you walk past the guards, a short branching corridor leads you to another door prominently marked in Aztec:

Montezuma's Monster Menagerie
(Admittance Free)

Pushing through it, the smell hits you at once, as does the noise. The chamber is dimly lit so it takes a moment for your eyes to adjust. But then you see it.

This huge chamber is lined with cages and in the cages are all manner of peculiar things. In one you see a two-headed wildcat. Another houses a deer that looks quite normal until you notice its five legs. Another holds Siamese twins, another a giant albino frog.

You can scarcely believe the creatures you see here, a mix of human freaks and abnormal animals. And you can scarcely believe the conditions in which they are kept. Their cages are filthy, they live in perpetual gloom and they look half-starved.

Appalled, you walk along the line of cages. You are more determined than ever to help overthrow the Aztec Empire.

Then suddenly you stop, as if struck by a thunderbolt, your eyes locked on two miserable creatures confined to a tiny cage in one corner. For a moment you are utterly unable to believe your eyes. You move closer, convinced your sight must be deceiving you. But there is no doubt. You are looking at your own parents!

"Mum, Dad," you gasp. "What are you doing here?"

They stare out at you with empty eyes. "Is ... is that you, Hummingbird?" your mother asks weakly.

"It's me. It's me. But what happened? Why are you here?"

Your father stirs fitfully, then speaks in a dry, feeble voice. "Montezuma thought you'd hear about us and give yourself up."

"But you mustn't do that," your mother puts in. "We're fine."

"You're not fine here, Mum," you tell her firmly. "But I'll get you out!"

"That may be easier said than done," your father remarks. "The controls that open these cages aren't even in this room."

"Where are they?"

"If you take the branch corridor just before you come into this chamber, the controls are down there somewhere," your father says. "Only I'm not sure exactly where."

"I'll find them," you promise, and you are through the door in a flash, racing down the branching corridor.

Which unfortunately leads to no less than four stout doors, each of which has a guard stationed outside. The doors open, respectively, onto 109, 128, 140 and 156. None of them has any indication of what might be inside. And by the way, the guards are armed and watching you intently.

Montezuma looks up in surprise as you re-enter his throne room. "Forgotten something?" he asks. "If we're not careful, we'll forget our *heart* next!"

You're not slow to take a hint, so you give a sickly smile and assure him you're just going again.

Which you can do by backing out the door and making the choice of going north to 72, east to 84, or through the door to 104.

You stand like an ostrich with your head stuck in the hole in the altar. After a while you take it out again.

Go back to 97 and try something else.

You saunter up to the soldiers. "Hi, fellas, what's happening?"

The nearest warrior, a big burly fellow with a boss eye, looks past you at a point in the sky somewhere over your right shoulder. "Some young guttersnipe's trying to escape."

"What's this person done?" you ask.

"This person has avoided being sacrificed," the warrior growls. "Worst crime in the book, except for one."

"What's that?" you ask curiously.

"Getting our leave cancelled," he tells you sourly. "We don't like that. So we've decided to give a hard time to anybody who tries to get past us. Specially when they're young and innocent." The boss eye shifts so that it's staring at a spot about the level of your left kneecap. "You're not young and innocent, are you?"

"No," you say quickly, "Of course not. I mean, I'm young but not innocent. I mean, I'm not guilty either, but …"

The boss eye never wavers from your kneecap as he watches you hurry all the way to 19 to pick another destination.

121

The door pushes open and you step inside to what appears to be an old store room filled with junk of every description.

It occurs to you that it might be worth a search, but you hesitate, unwilling to spend too much time in a room that Montezuma expressly told you not to visit.

If you decide to search this room, you can do so at 113. Or you can go back out to the corridor where you have the choice of the door on the left to 107, the door on the right to 136, or returning up the corridor to the point where you join with the corridor running north to 72 and the door opening into 104.

122

Swiftly you scoop up the tin money, then swing round, senses highly alert, waiting for a devastating supernatural attack.

But none comes. Which isn't surprising since the Nezahual is just the statue of a mangy old coyote, not some powerful prehistoric god. You now have fully fifty tin Ts, which could come in handy for bribing somebody some time. Stow your loot and leave the shrine to climb the steps to the top of the larger pyramid at 155, or climb all the way back down to 52.

123

You push into the undergrowth. The maracas grow louder.

You reach an open archway leading into the remains of an ancient stone building. The building seems to have been a little temple at one time, because there's a massive stone carving of a rattlesnake on the one remaining intact wall. You leap gaily through the archway.

You wish you hadn't.

That carving should have given you the clue. Maracas were only brought to South America with the Africans, who haven't arrived yet. The sound that lured you here was the warning of a rattlesnake.

This interesting reptile has 30 Life Points, and strikes at only +1 fang damage, which doesn't sound so bad, but if it manages to fang you twice running, you'll find yourself at 13 with poison running out of your ears, which sounds absolutely awful.

In the unlikely event that you survive, turn to 106.

"Sounds good to me," says one guard.

"Sounds good to me," says the other.

"Unless," says the first, frowning, "your name happens to be Hummingbird. It's not Hummingbird is it?"

"Definitely not," you tell them quickly.

"That's all right then. Pass, friend!"

And they step to one side, allowing you to enter the Monster Menagerie at 117.

"Let me try to help you!" you say.

"How are you going to do that?" he asks curiously.

"I have come to the conclusion that the way out is via Section 10. There you may find a road back to the major highways." You hesitate. "Of course, I can't guarantee you won't be stopped by Aztec soldiers, in which case you'll need a special pass."

"Special pass is no problem," he tells you delightedly. "I noticed a couple hidden at the Pyramid of the Sun. Please accept this as a token of my ambassadorial gratitude."

He hands you a container of fermented cactus and races off.

That juice is something else. Drink it and you'll get an immediate boost of 30 Life Points on top of what you have now (or whenever you drink), even if you were already at your maximum. Worth having, especially if you're heading for a tricky fight. Now go to 33 and select another destination.

Excitedly you pull back the tapestry. You stand bewildered. There's no secret panel here – only a blank wall on which someone has inscribed a few Aztec hieroglyphs. Then it occurs to you that the whole point of a secret panel is it has to be secret. You beat your head against the wall at your own stupidity, and note the hollow sound that means either there's definitely a hidden panel or your brains have fallen out. Then you begin painfully to decipher the Aztec hieroglyphs.

To activate panel multiply the number of days in an Aztec month by the number of days in an Aztec week, add three times the number of months in an Aztec year, then subtract one and go to the Section number you've calculated.

If you can work out the number, turn to the section that lets you open the secret panel. If not, your only option is to leave this room and try the doors at 109, 128, or 156. If you've no joy there, you can always wander back up the corridor to 84.

"Yeech!" you yell as you start to run around in circles like a headless chicken. "Help! Save me! I don't want to die!"

And so on for quite a long time.

None of which does you the slightest good, so you might as well apply a little curtain therapy (ie, pull yourself together) and tackle the real issues of the approaching guard at 148 or searching for your parents at 134.

To your surprise, the guard smiles as you approach.

"Welcome, pilgrim, to the temple of Tezcatlipoca," he calls cheerfully. "I can't tell you how pleased we are to see you!"

With which he ushers you hurriedly through the door and closes it behind you. You look around and your stomach turns over. This chamber is packed with human skulls. There are hundreds of them, thousands of them. Most are bleached white, but a few aren't all that old, so that bits of skin are still sticking to them and the smell of decay is pretty awful.

In fact it's so awful it's already cost you a Life Point due to nausea. All the same, it might be worth searching the place, at the cost of a further 5 Life Points, at 116. Or you can go back and pick one of the other three doors at 109, 140 or 156.

129

It's so dark in here you begin to wonder if the foul smell is so strong it's absorbing the light. But you push this ridiculous thought from your mind and stride forward.

Into the cesspit Aztec pilgrims have used for generations!!

Let's deal with this one disaster at a time. First, roll two dice to see if you drown. Anything under six and you do: go to 13. Six or more and you survive to face your next problem.

Roll the dice again to see if you survive swallowing an enormous curdled mouthful of you know what. Anything under five and you get sick and die: go to 13. Five or more and you survive to face your next problem.

Make an Absolutely Anything Roll to find out if you can climb successfully out of this cesspit. If you die in the attempt, go to 13. If you fail permanently, drown horribly and go to 13. If you succeed, make your smelly way to 7.

130

Dumb move. Your chest locks tight. Your breath rasps. Your knees turn to jelly. Your legs begin to tremble. The torch goes out. Your fingers go numb. There are bright lights before your eyes. Your head aches. Your teeth chatter. Your toes curl. Your hair falls out. Your arches drop. Your feet splay.

Throw two dice and deduct the total from your Life Points. If this kills you, go to 13. Otherwise go to 105 and try another exit, unless you want to search for a secret passage at 111.

You eyeball the guards menacingly. "Better let him go," you say, "Otherwise I shall be forced to use physical violence."

They keep grinning broadly.

"And I'd better warn you I've considerable experience of dealing with louts like you."

They keep grinning broadly.

It looks as if you're not going to talk them into a surrender, so let's get on with the fight. Each guard has been pumping iron so long that he's reached the maximum of 60 Life Points, while the swords they carry hit with +5. They're wearing quilted cotton armour which, while not the best, is still good enough to deduct 3 from any damage scored against them. If you survive this brutally uneven contest, you may lick your wounds at 150. If not you'll have to lick them at 13.

You close your eyes, screw up your face and cautiously move the lever.

Nothing happens.

You move it a little further.

Nothing happens.

With a sudden surge of courage, you move it all the way.

Nothing happens.

You stand staring at the lever, wondering if you've moved it the wrong way.

Only one way to find out – just slam the lever violently in the other direction at 138. Alternatively, of course, you can take time to check if anything's happened in the Monster Menagerie at 157.

"Stop right there!" you growl menacingly. "Harm one hair on his chest and you'll have me to answer to!"

The priest with the knife stares at you in amazement, then begins to giggle. "Be still, my beating heart!" he exclaims. "I'm soooooo frightened!"

The other five priests start to laugh uproariously as well. "You deal with this idiot, Huex," says the one at the boy's head to the priest holding the knife. "We'll hold the kid down until you've finished off the lunatic."

Well, at least you're not fighting all six of them. In fact, you're only fighting Huex, the priest with the obsidian knife, for now. Huex has 50 Life Points and that knife is so sharp it strikes with +8. As against that, he's now laughing so much you get the first strike automatically, which must be worth something. If Huex kills you, go to 13. If you manage to rid the world of Huex, you can face up to the other five priests at 151.

You take a deep breath and plunge into the mêlée. Monsters crowd against you from every side.

Behind you the sound of running footsteps grows louder. And more ominously, it also sounds as if more and more people are coming at the double. You press on with renewed vigour, hurling monsters aside in your anxiety to find your folks.

Eventually, with enormous difficulty, you reach the cage where your parents were held. The door is open and it is empty.

"Mum! Dad!" you scream.

The only answer is howls from the monsters as scores of burly guards crash through the door. You swing round to meet them and discover to your horror they are led by ten of Montezuma's most bloodthirsty priests.

You resignedly meet your fate at 13.

The passageway emerges into a large room filled with an enormous hoard of golden artefacts. But despite this mountain of gold, your eyes go at once to the couple seated together on a golden bench in one corner.

"Mum, Dad," you gasp. "You're safe!"

Your father nods. "Tezcatlipoca got us out just after the cage door opened. Your mother wanted to wait for you, but I told her it would be better if you rescued us personally after such a long and exciting adventure."

"In fact, it may actually be necessary," Tezcatlipoca murmurs.

"What do you mean?" you cry.

"The only way out of this place is through Section 149," Tezcatlipoca tells you. "It's a small chamber leading to a tunnel that will take us right out of the city. The trouble is there's a guard in the chamber. Just one, but the place is too small for any more than one of us to fight him. You can still be the one who rescues your parents."

You grin broadly, "Lead me to him!"

Your mother proudly looks on as you make your way to 149.

The door opens at a push like most Aztec doors, but at once your way is blocked by two huge guards.

"What's the password?" one demands.

"It's the name of the goddess of Earth, Life and Death," whispers the other as a hint.

"So it has to be Coatlicue or Huitzilopochtli," grins the first.

If you give the password as 'Coatlicue' turn to 124. If you think it might be 'Huitzilopochtli', try 154. If you decide you don't want to worry about some stupid password, you can get into a fight with them at 110.

137

Mmm, not much to see here, if you don't count those T-shaped bits of tin in the stone bowl at the feet of that crumbling old statue of a Nezahual ...

You suddenly stop this rambling (and intensely boring) stream of consciousness. T-shaped bits of tin are one of the forms of money used by the Aztecs! That bowl must be an offering dish used during their pilgrimages to this ancient ruined city.

The question is, do you feel like robbing an offering dish and possibly offending the Nezahual? If so, try grabbing the loot at 122. If you'd prefer not to risk it, you can leave this broken-down little shrine and climb the steps to the pyramid's top at 155, or climb all the way back down to 52.

138

You close your eyes, screw up your face and cautiously move the lever.

Boom!

Well, there goes the universe. Go to 13.

139

You stand for a moment, locked in indecision.

Tezcatlipoca actually grabs your shoulders and shakes you. "There are guards coming!" he screams in your ear. "Hundreds of them! Priests as well! Montezuma's found out who you are! If you stay here a minute longer, it's Section 13 for you for sure!"

This is nerve-wracking! If Tezcatlipoca's right, if you hang around you'll all be killed by the guards. But as against that there's a chance you might get your parents out before the guards arrive. But as against that, it's you the guards want ...

Listen, you don't have time for this! Either you're off with Tezcatlipoca at 152 or you're into the monster mêlée to find your folks at 134.

To your surprise, the guard smiles as you approach.

"Welcome, pilgrim, to the temple of Huitzilopochtli," he calls cheerfully. "I can't tell you how pleased we are to see you!"

With which he ushers you quickly through the door and closes it.

You stop, open-mouthed. If Montezuma's throne room was impressive, it's nothing to what's going on here. Seated on an immense throne of what looks like solid gold is a handsome youth about your own age or perhaps just a little older. He is dressed in a wonderful featherwork cloak and head-dress, a jewel-encrusted loincloth, he has golden sandals on his feet, and wears heavily jewelled rings and earrings. His body glistens with expensive oils. Young though he is, he looks more of an Emperor than the Emperor himself.

A score or more individuals (including four very attractive young girls) are ranged around him in postures of worship and adoration. This character has all the hallmarks of a god!

He looks at you with large brown eyes. "Help," he says.

Help? This divine goon wants your help? The call for help has to be some sort of trick, right? If you want to fall for it, you can offer him help at 158. If not, this effete bunch will not stop you searching the room, which you can do at 114.

Not much here except empty boxes, lots of junk and the body of a snake. But you do come on a scrap of paper on which somebody has written:

The password is Huitzilopochtli.

Not much immediate help! Since there's nothing else here, you better go back out to the corridor where you have the choice of the door on the left to 107, the door on the right to 136, or returning back up the corridor to the point where you join with the corridor running north to 72 and the door opening to 104.

Hey, it's working! The skunk slowly turns, then polishes your ankle like a cat. All the textbooks say this is quite impossible! Now the little fella's lying on his back, waiting for his tummy to be tickled. When you oblige, he skeeters off and brings you back a small clay tablet on which is inscribed a Toltec Death Spell.

Frankly I think you lucked out on this one. You can find out about the Toltec Death Spell just two sections ahead at 144. When you come back here, you have the choice of entering the large pyramid at 137, climbing the steps to the top of the large pyramid at 155, or climbing all the way back down to 52.

You smile weakly. "Pleased to meet you, Your Divinity. Now, if you'll excuse me, I have to help overthrow the Aztec Empire."

"No, please, don't go," pleads Tezcatlipoca. "You must help!"

At which his followers begin to move menacingly in your direction. You turn to make a break for the door.

Time for an Absolutely Anything Roll again! If you die in your attempt, go to 13. If you succeed, then you're outside with the choice of hiding in any one of the rooms beyond the three remaining doors to 109, 128, or 156. If you fail, I'm afraid you'll have to hear the lunatic out at 115.

144

This vicious little item used to wipe out whole armies in the Toltec heyday, but a lot of the energy has seeped away over the past thousand years. Yet even now, reading the spell aloud will cause one human enemy to explode messily without your having to lay a finger on him. The spell can only be used once.

Now return to the section where you found it.

145

You're getting good at this. When you search the bodies of the two priests, you discover pouches of some peculiar substance which turns out to be dried cinchona bark, but apart from the little casket, there's nothing else of interest in this chamber.

Although what you have is interesting enough. First off, the bark will restore a die roll of Life Points when chewed. Roll two dice to find out how many chewable doses there are. Next, the book in the casket contains a single die roll of Toltec Death Spells (read about them in Section 144) each of which you can use once. And finally, you're welcome to the +5 knives the priests were using. Having got through that lot, you can now trog off to take your pick of the doors leading to 109, 128 or 140.

146

Your companion presses the hieroglyph. Nothing happens.

"Again!" you scream frantically. "Press it again!"

"It's no good," Tezcatlipoca gasps. "It must be the other – "

At which the entrance to the secret passage opens suddenly with a grinding of stone on stone.

Tezcatlipoca grabs you and pulls you in, then works a mechanism that closes the passage off again. You hear the pursuing guards and priests thundering past the secret entrance.

"Safe," sighs Tezcatlipoca. "Now come with me – there's somebody you have to meet."

And for once with no decision to make, you allow him to lead you down the secret passage all the way to 135.

Your companion presses the hieroglyph. Nothing happens.

"The other one! The other one!" you scream frantically.

But alas it's too late. Before either of you can so much as move a finger, a tidal wave of priests and guards sweeps down the passageway venting a communal howl of rage and blood-lust.

And sweeping you both, I regret to say, all the way back to 13.

You swing round, ready to defend yourself.

Fortunately there's only one approaching figure.

You begin to scrabble for a weapon, then stop. The running figure is the young man you rescued, the one forced to play Tezcatlipoca.

"What are you doing here?" you ask in amazement. "I thought you'd be long gone by now."

"No time to explain," he gasps. "You must come at once!"

Decisions! Decisions! Are you going to go with Tezcatlipoca to 139? Or will you ignore this breathless lad and plunge amongst the monsters to try to find your folks at 134?

Tezcatlipoca was right about the chamber. There's just about room for two people. The guard is absolutely enormous (and wearing a tiny golden key around his neck for some reason).

"Where d'you think you're going, Pipsqueak?" he asks rudely.

"Into this tunnel," you reply.

"Oh yeah?"

"Oh yeah!"

And so on until you're both worked up into a fighting frenzy.

At which point you need to know this huge goon has 70 Life Points. His sword hacks at +8 and he's carrying a featherwork shield which subtracts 3 from damage scored against him. If you get the better of him, take his little golden key and proceed swiftly to 160. If you don't, leave the key alone and proceed equally swiftly to 13.

That was some fight! But now everyone in the chamber is applauding you excitedly. Even Tezcatlipoca is applauding you. He races forward, throws his arms around you and kisses you. "Thank you!" he exclaims. "Thank you! Thank you!"

You fight your way free of this unseemly display of emotion, muttering, "It was nothing really."

"Nothing?" exclaims Tezcatlipoca. "I owe you everything I have, which is more or less nothing now, since I need to get out of here promptly and hide until they elect the next Tezcatlipoca on Thursday. But you're welcome to all my gear."

He places his cloak, head-dress, rings, and so on, at your feet.

"Is there anything else I can do for you before I go?" he cries.

"I don't suppose you'd know where I can find the machinery that unlocks the cages in Montezuma's Monster Menagerie by any chance?" you ask.

"Of course I do!" Tezcatlipoca exclaims. "It's behind a secret panel hidden by that tapestry!" He points at a wall-hanging which depicts a room with a secret panel hidden by a tapestry.

Then, before you can so much as thank him, Tezcatlipoca and his entourage stampede from the room. You turn towards the tapestry that hides the secret panel.

But before you do anything about that, roll two dice and multiply the result by ten to discover the worth (in quills of gold dust) of all that junk Tezcatlipoca left you. When you've made a note of the result, feel free to hurry on to 126 where you can examine the secret panel.

The priests stare at you.

"Huex is dead!" one gasps.

"Our visitor is obviously favoured by the gods!" exclaims the first.

With which they release the boy and drop to their knees, bowing and scraping furiously in your direction.

Hardly able to believe your luck, you look over to the boy on the pyramid.

"Thanks for the rescue," he says, racing across the room. He hesitates at the door. "I've a feeling the room you want has something to do with the world's soul," he says mysteriously, before disappearing into the corridor outside.

To which you can now follow him in order to select one of the three remaining guarded doors – 128, 140 and 156.

"You're right!" you say, as Tezcatlipoca grabs your arm and drags you through the door to the Monster Menagerie. A little way up the corridor you can hear scores of running footsteps.

"Not there for sure!" grins Tezcatlipoca, nodding towards the approaching noise. "We're taking a secret passage." He stops.

"What?" you ask, suddenly suspicious. "What? What?"

"Well," says Texcatlipoca uneasily, "It's just that I've forgotten the hieroglyph to press to open it. I know it's the one for the god of war, but I can't remember whether that's Huitzilopochtli or Azcapozalco. I don't suppose you know, do you?"

Another dumb memory test! But what can you do? Well, actually, all you really can do is choose between the Huitzilopochtli at 146 and Azcapozalco next door at 147.

There's a sharp click. The Aztec hieroglyphs flash several times and a small panel in the wall begins slowly to slide back.

Behind the panel is a lever marked:

← Master Control →
Please move one way to open cages in Monster Menagerie and the other way to destroy the universe.

You stare at this lunatic message. Then you remember hearing that the reason the Aztecs were so big into human sacrifice was that they were worried about the end of the world, which falls short of the destruction of the universe, but only just.

You find yourself growing strangely uneasy. Is it possible the priests know how to destroy the universe? Is it possible that if you move the lever the wrong way, you will wipe out the whole of creation? This is very difficult to believe, but all the same ...

Suddenly it becomes extremely important for you to figure out which way the lever moves to open the monster cages and which way will destroy the universe, if indeed, it's possible to destroy the whole universe just by moving a stupid Aztec lever.

Despite the urgency to free your parents, you leave the lever severely alone while you scrabble about in the bottom of the secret cupboard in a frenzied attempt to find some helpful clue. Sure enough, your hand hits on a piece of aloe-leaf paper on which are written the words:

If nequem cloth is made from aloe thread, you can safely move the lever to the right. Otherwise moving the lever to the right will destroy the universe.
Signed,
One Who Knows These Things.

This is the sort of message guaranteed to send you bats. But you have to take life as you find it, and if you're going to rescue your folks, you have to move that lever. So are you going to move it to the right at 132 or to the left at 138?

"Wrong! And after all the hints we gave you," remarks one, shaking his head sadly.

And they sling you out and slam the door.

Which leaves you with the choice of the door in the middle to 121, the door on the left to 107, or returning back up the corridor to the point where the corridor runs north to 72 and the door opens into 104. Or you can beat their heads in at 110.

Some view from up here. You can see all the way along the Street of the Dead, as the Aztecs insist on calling it. It runs directly north-south, forming the main axis of the ancient city. The road points all the way towards the hallowed mountain, Cerro Gordo, which lies behind the pyramid on which you now stand, nearly fifty metres above the ground.

You are bewitched by the place. The Street of the Dead is at least fifty metres wide. Down below are dozens of platforms, minor pyramids, staircases and other structures ranging towards the volcanic outcrops of the southern horizon.

To your left, half way along, towers the mighty Pyramid of the Sun, the largest building of its type in the whole of the Aztec Empire, bigger even than the monstrous pyramid temples the Aztecs themselves built.

And right beside you towers that ugly looking stone statue you saw earlier. It looks a lot like Huitzilopochtli, the Aztec's God of War and patron of their nation.

Which it may be since there's a little arms cache at its base. You find a bow and seven arrows, and a vest of quilted cotton. Each arrow does +5 damage, allowing you first strike and no worries about getting hit back (unless your opponent has a bow as well). You can only use each of these arrows once, but hold onto the bow in case you find any more.

The vest is so well made that it neutralises the plus factor of any thrown weapon (e.g. javelin or spear) or shot weapon (e.g. arrow) except for firearms. So if you're attacked by bows or spears while wearing this vest, your opponent will score dice damage only. Now off to 33 to pick another destination.

156

To your surprise, the guard smiles as you approach.

"Welcome, pilgrim, to the temple of Coatlicue," he calls cheerfully. "I can't tell you how pleased we are to see you!"

Three figures look up as you enter. And smile.

You're in a wad of trouble. These are three priests polishing up their sacrificial knives. There's no avoiding a punch-up. Each priest has 30 Life Points and those knives strike at +5. The only good news is that none of them is wearing armour, so any blow you get in does full damage.

But before you leap into battle you could look at a small bound book of aloe leaf papyrus, lying just inside the door at 108, but only at a cost of allowing one of the priests an automatic first strike against you.
Otherwise you get an automatic first strike against all three since they weren't expecting you.

If the encounter kills you, go to 13. If you survive, it's onwards to 145.

Eagerly you push through the door marked:

Montezuma's Monster Menagerie
(Admittance Free)

Something's happened all right! There's a full-scale riot going on in here. You stand there stunned, then you realise that the lever didn't just open the cage holding your parents – it opened *every* cage, and the monsters are now charging around. Some of the wilder ones are fighting. The place has turned into a nightmare.

"Mum! Dad!" you call. But your voice is drowned by the turmoil.

Behind you is the sound of running footsteps: opening the monster cages must have set off an alarm somewhere!

"MUM! DAD!" you call again, straining your eyes in the half light to catch sight of them in this panic-stricken crowd.

Still there is no reply. You've obviously got to do something quickly. But what? What? What, what, what?

You can panic completely at 127. Or you can tackle the guard (or guards) you've just heard running down the corridor behind you at 148. Or you can plunge in among the rioting monsters and try to find your folks at 134.

"What can I do for you, Your … Majesty? … Holiness?"

The youth shakes his jewelled head sadly. "The title is 'Soul of the World', but no ceremony now! I'm in more than enough trouble without that. You know the god Tezcatlipoca?"

"Not personally," you tell him, "but I know who you mean."

"Well," says the youth, "I am Tezcatlipoca."

A nutter! Maybe you should make a break for it before he turns violent, a course of action you may take at 143. Alternatively, you can stick around and take your chances listening to the rest of this fairy story at 115.

"It's a deal," you say. "I've always known I could run rings round Maradonna if only somebody would give me the chance!"

With which you drop your weapons to the ground and welcome your fate with open arms. At which point fifty-one heavily armed and armoured warriors, led by a smiling man in flash gold and silver armour, all step onto the road and fall into place around you.

I'm not sure this is necessarily the best decision you've ever made. We'll soon find out if you turn to 11.

HUMMINGBIRD TRIUMPHANT

News of your great adventure has obviously preceded you, for the streets of your native village are lined with cheering crowds. Behind you, your parents (staggering under the weight of booty liberated from the secret treasure room) beam with pride.

The chief of your tribe steps forward and clears his throat. "Hummingbird," he says loudly, "in recognition of your truly incredible performance against the Aztecs, admittedly after quite a bad start, I hereby award you the Freedom of the Village!"

"Thank you, sir, but it was nothing really," you tell him.

"So modest," you hear an admiring whisper from the crowd.

"Better get some rest now," the chief advises. "We've laid on a banquet for later."

And so they have. That evening you sit down to a meal worthy of the mad Montezuma himself – roast turkey served with goblets of chocolatl flavoured with vanilla and spices.

"Tell me something, oh Young Person of the Hour," says the guest on your right, some minor chieftain from a neighbouring tribe, "What is that small gold key around your neck?"

"Perhaps it's the key to that little golden casket I notice sticking out of your tote bag," suggests a woman on your left.

"Perhaps it is," you say and take out the casket you found in the secret compartment of the altar on top of the Pyramid of the Sun in Teotihuacán. It seems a lifetime ago now.

You place the key in the lock and the casket springs open.

"What's in there?" asks the woman, peering over your shoulder.

You reach in and draw out some ancient sheets of aloe-leaf paper. The writing is faded and hard to make out, but you strain your keen young eyes and eventually it grows clear. "Good grief," you exclaim. "These are ancient Toltec prophecies, lost for centuries." You lean closer and begin to read avidly.

The remaining guests move into a circle around you. "What do they say?" asks your chief.

Frowning, you look up. "They foretell that they, the Toltecs, will disappear and be replaced by a vast and blood-thirsty empire built on human sacrifice."

"The Aztec Empire!" someone whispers.

"They say that in the Year of 1-Reed, invaders will arrive from the East – "

"The Spanish invasion," whispers someone else.

" – and they will utterly destroy the blood-thirsty empire."

There is a spontaneous burst of cheering and a general quaffing of medicinal pulque. But you hold up your hand for silence. "I'm afraid they also say the invaders will be as cruel as the Aztecs, and will bring much death and disease with them."

Your chief shrugs. "I'll take my chance on that," he says. "Nothing could be worse than Montezuma." He reaches for your plate. "Put the papers away, Hummingbird, and let me help you to a heap more turkey."

GAME PLAY SYSTEM
Here's what you'll need to survive this book:

Life Points

Roll one of your dice and multiply the result by ten to give you a Life Point figure between 10 and 60. You're allowed to do this three times and pick the best score out of the three.

Fights

First attack: In any combat situation, begin by rolling one of your dice. Score 4, 5 or 6 and the first attack is yours. Score 1, 2 or 3 and your opponent gets to go first.

Striking blows: Roll both dice to strike a blow or use a weapon. Score 2, 3 or 4 and it counts as a miss. Anything else is a hit and the score comes off your opponent's Life Points. Throw the dice for your opponent in exactly the same way. Any hits scored by him come off your Life Points.

Weapons: If you (or your opponent) are using a weapon, it adds extra damage to a successful hit. The amount of extra damage is given with the weapon. For example, if you find a +5 pistol, it means each time you successfully shoot somebody with it, you add 5 to the damage shown by the dice.

Ammunition: Firearms are useless without ammo. You'll be told when you find a weapon how much ammo it contains. Once out of ammo, you score no extra damage when using a firearm.

Healing

Medicine: Medicine restores Life Points. You'll be told how to calculate the number of restored Points with each medical pack.

Rest: If you can't find medicine when you need it, you can always take a chance on resting. You can rest any time and as often as you like. To do so, throw one of your dice. Score 5 or 6 and you can add that number to your Life Points. Score 3 or 4 and you deduct that number, because you were attacked in your sleep. Score 1 or 2 and you rested without being attacked, but were too nervous to restore any Life Points.

Death

When your Life Points come down to zero, you're dead and you have to start the adventure again from the beginning. When any opponent's Life Points reach zero, they too are dead.

Money

Keep a careful note of any money you may earn or find during your adventure. It could be useful for buying things or (occasionally) bribery.

Experience

Every time you win a fight (and in a few other special circumstances as well) you earn one Experience Point. Keep careful note of the total: 10 Experience Points gives you a Special Life Point. Special Life Points are added to your total just like ordinary Life Points and are lost in fights just like ordinary Life Points. However, if you're killed during an adventure, you can add all your Special Life Points to your score when you're rolling up your Life Points for the next try.

You can add Special Life Points even if you score the absolute maximum of 60 when you're rolling your Life Points. So if you have earned 6 Special Life Points and score 60 on your Life Point roll, your final Life Points will be 66.

Special Life Points carry over to other books in this series.

Absolutely Anything Roll

From time to time during your adventure, you might want to try to do something weird or spectacular. To find out the result, use the Absolutely Anything Roll. Throw both dice.

• Score 2 and you failed to do what you tried to do and killed yourself in the attempt.

• Score 3, 4 or 5 and you failed to do what you tried to do and can't try again.

• Score 6, 7, 8 or 9 and you failed to do what you tried to do but can try just one more time.

• Score 10, 11 or 12 and you succeed.

GLOSSARY

Aztlan
Legends tell of how the Aztecs came from Aztlan in Northern Mexico and settled in the valley, where they founded Tenochtitlán.

Hieroglyphs
Picture symbols used for writing.

Huitzilopochtli
The Aztecs believed the god Huitzilopochtli had told them where to build the city of Tenochtitlán.

Invaders from the East
In 1519, a group of about 500 Spanish soldiers, (*conquistadors*), led by Hernán Cortés, attacked the Aztecs.

Maguey
A plant native to Mexico.

Mayans
The Mayan Indians created a magnificent civilization, in what is now called southern Mexico and Guatemala, as long ago as 2000 B.C.

Montezuma II
The ruler of the Aztecs at the time of the *conquistadors*.

Pyramid of the Sun
Built around A.D. 50 in Teotihuacán. It was the largest building in the Americas until the arrival of the Europeans.

Quetzal
A golden green Central American bird, with very long tail feathers.

Quetzalcóatl
The chief god of the people of Teotihuacán, often shown as a feathered serpent. This was a kindly god, uniting the forces of the world.

Tenochtitlán
The city which the Aztecs started to build in 1325. It is built on an island in Lake Texcoco, and is now the site of Mexico city.

Teotihuacán
The largest city in the Mayan civilization.

Tezcatlipoca
The Toltec god of pleasure and sin, the enemy of Quetzalcóatl.

Tlaxcala
An Aztec town.